FUZZY ANIMALS

Lincoln
Children's Books

Brimming with creative inspiration, how-to projects, and useful information to enrich your everyday life, Quarto Knows is a favourite destination for those pursuing their interests and passions. Visit our site and dig deeper with our books into your area of interest: Quarto Creates, Quarto Cooks, Quarto Homes, Quarto Lives, Quarto Drives, Quarto Explores, Quarto Gifts, or Quarto Kids.

First Published in 2018 by Lincoln Children's Books,
an imprint of The Quarto Group.
The Old Brewery, 6 Blundell Street, London N7 9BH, United Kingdom.
T (0)20 7700 6700 F (0)20 7700 8066 **www.QuartoKnows.com**

Published in association with the Natural History Museum, London.

A catalogue record for this book is available from the British Library.

ISBN 978-1-78603-162-4

The illustrations were painted in watercolour and edited digitally.
Set in Futura and Livifont2017.

Published by Rachel Williams and Jenny Broom
Designed by Karissa Santos
Edited by Katy Flint
Production by Laura Grandi

Manufactured in Shenzhen, China, HH022018

9 8 7 6 5 4 3 2 1

How To Use This Book

There are **seven** colouring charts in this book.

Each animal on the colouring chart has a number.

Lifespan: 12 years
Diet: Small mammals, birds and reptiles
Skill: It leaps and pounces on prey from a great height.

Match each number to the Fact File on the opposite page.

Read facts and get ideas for which colours to use from the pictures in the Fact Files. Do the animals have fur, feathers, spines or scales? How will you choose to colour them in?

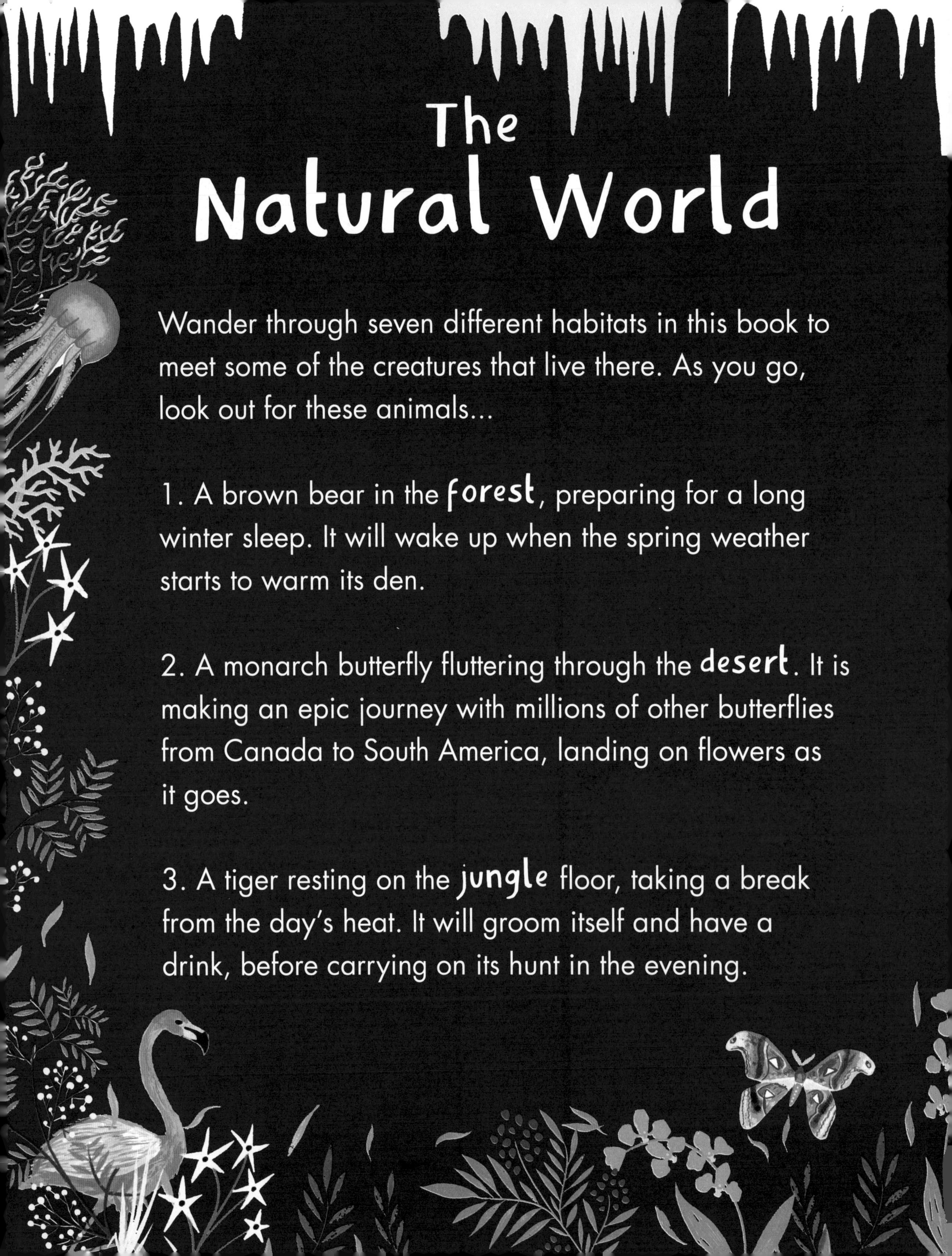

The Natural World

Wander through seven different habitats in this book to meet some of the creatures that live there. As you go, look out for these animals...

1. A brown bear in the forest, preparing for a long winter sleep. It will wake up when the spring weather starts to warm its den.

2. A monarch butterfly fluttering through the desert. It is making an epic journey with millions of other butterflies from Canada to South America, landing on flowers as it goes.

3. A tiger resting on the jungle floor, taking a break from the day's heat. It will groom itself and have a drink, before carrying on its hunt in the evening.

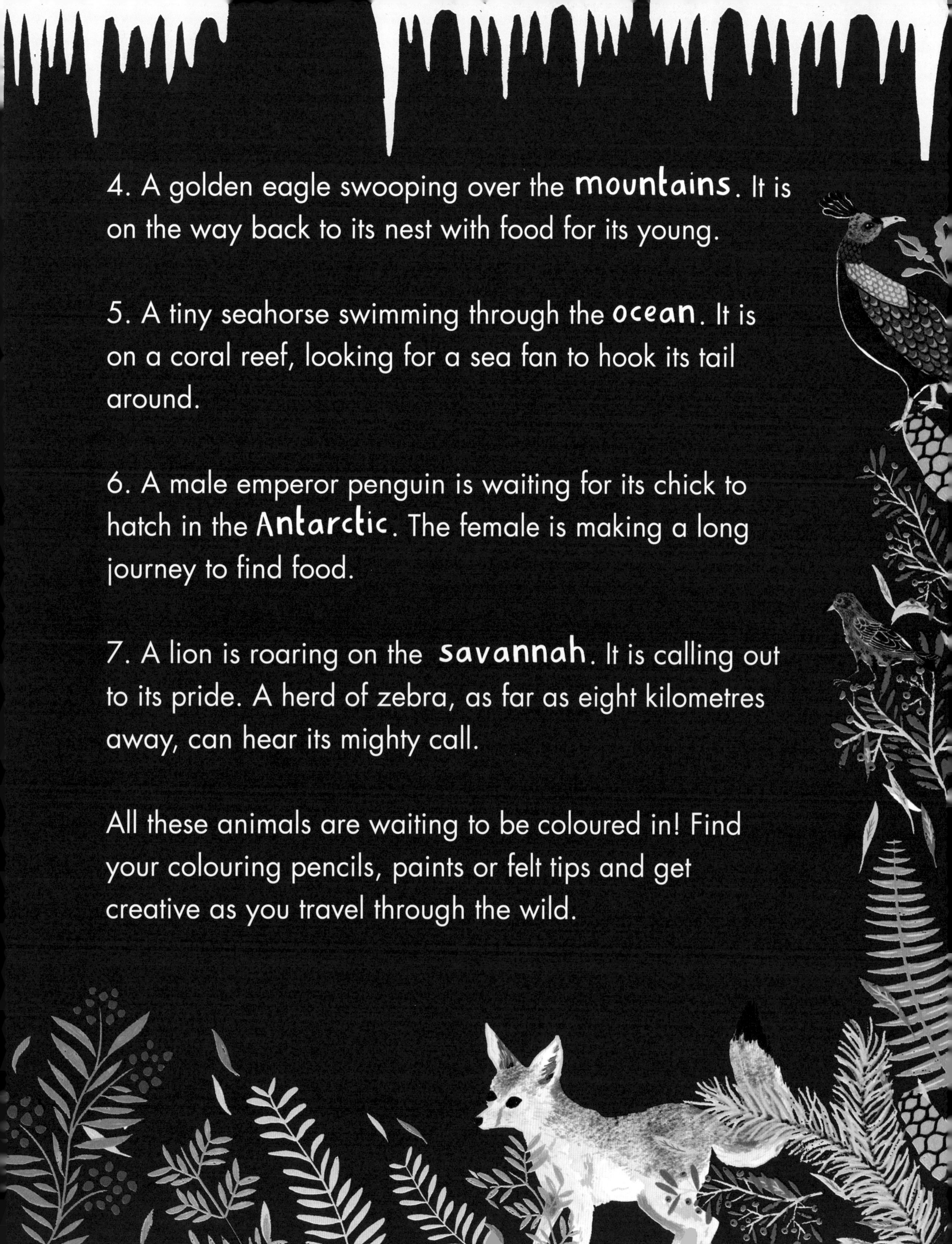

4. A golden eagle swooping over the **mountains**. It is on the way back to its nest with food for its young.

5. A tiny seahorse swimming through the **ocean**. It is on a coral reef, looking for a sea fan to hook its tail around.

6. A male emperor penguin is waiting for its chick to hatch in the **Antarctic**. The female is making a long journey to find food.

7. A lion is roaring on the **savannah**. It is calling out to its pride. A herd of zebra, as far as eight kilometres away, can hear its mighty call.

All these animals are waiting to be coloured in! Find your colouring pencils, paints or felt tips and get creative as you travel through the wild.

Forest

These animals live in the forests of the U.S.A. and Canada. Colour them in!

1 Owl

Lifespan: 7 years
Diet: Mice and insects
Skill: It silently swoops down on prey and grabs it with its sharp talons.

2 Crossbill

Lifespan: 2 years
Diet: Seeds
Skill: Its upper and lower bill cross over so it can prise open pine cones and eat the seeds.

3 Bobcat

Lifespan: 12 years
Diet: Small mammals, birds and reptiles
Skill: It leaps and pounces on prey from a great height.

4 Raccoon

Lifespan: 3 years
Diet: Fruits, plants, insects and much more
Skill: The fingers on their front feet help them untie knots, turn doorknobs and open jars.

5 Porcupine

Lifespan: 6 years
Diet: Leaves, twigs, plants, bark and buds
Skill: Its sharp spines provide protection from predators.

6 Brown bear

Lifespan: 25 years
Diet: Plants, insects, fish and small animals
Skill: It can go into a deep sleep for months at a time in the winter.

1
2
3
4
5
6

Desert

These animals live in the desert in North America and Mexico. Colour them in!

Lifespan: 7 years
Diet: Rodents and small mammals
Skill: They do not need to drink water as they get it from their prey.

Lifespan: 1–2 weeks
Diet: Nectar
Skill: Its bright colours are a warning to predators that it tastes bad.

Lifespan: 2–6 weeks
Diet: Nectar
Skill: It pollinates the flowers of desert cacti when it lands on them.

Lifespan: 5–8 years
Diet: Insects and spiders
Skill: It stalks prey before lunging with its jaws.

Lifespan: 7 years
Diet: Smaller snakes, frogs and lizards
Skill: It startles enemies with a popping sound.

Lifespan: 6–8 years
Diet: Almost anything – rabbits, rodents, fish and frogs
Skill: It has a strong sense of smell and sight.

1
2
3
4
5
6

These creatures live in the jungle in Southeast Asia. Colour them in!

Lifespan: 2–3 years
Diet: Insects and birds
Skill: It shoots its very long tongue out to catch insects.

Lifespan: 25 years
Diet: Fruits, seeds, roots, herbs and insects
Skill: It is very good at climbing.

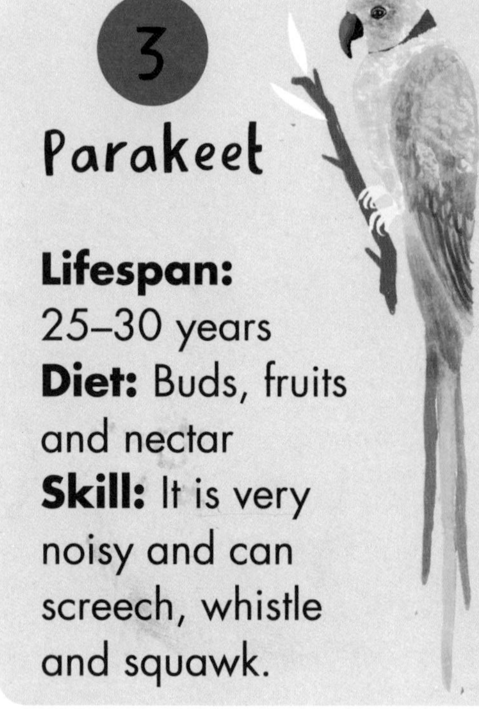

Lifespan: 25–30 years
Diet: Buds, fruits and nectar
Skill: It is very noisy and can screech, whistle and squawk.

Lifespan: 5–7 days
Diet: Adult moths do not eat.
Skill: They rely on stores of energy built up when they were caterpillars.

Lifespan: 10–15 years
Diet: Mostly deer-sized mammals
Skill: It has very good hearing and night vision.

1
2
3
4
5

Mountains

These animals live in and around the Himalayan mountains. Colour them in!

Lifespan: 3 years
Diet: Grasses, leaves and roots
Skill: The males attract females with their beautiful multicoloured feathers.

Lifespan: 30 years
Diet: Rabbits, reptiles, birds and dead meat
Skill: It snaps up prey with its sharp talons.

Lifespan: 12–14 years
Diet: Bamboo, insects and fruit
Skill: It blends in well with the reddish-brown moss of the fir trees it climbs.

Lifespan: 15–18 years
Diet: Sheep and goats
Skill: It stealthily attacks its prey from above or behind.

Lifespan: 20 years
Diet: Wildflowers, herbs and grass
Skill: It keeps warm with its long thick hair.

Lifespan: 20 years
Diet: Bamboo shoots
Skill: It can eat a large amount of bamboo, which it needs to do to survive.

1
2
3
4
5
6

Ocean

These animals live in oceans around the world. Colour them in!

Lifespan: 2–6 months
Diet: Plankton, snails and small fish
Skill: It swims using jet propulsion.

Lifespan: 20–30 years
Diet: Squid, octopus and other sharks
Skill: It stalks prey on the bottom of the ocean.

Lifespan: 3–6 years
Diet: Sea anemone
Skill: It dances before making its home in a sea anemone.

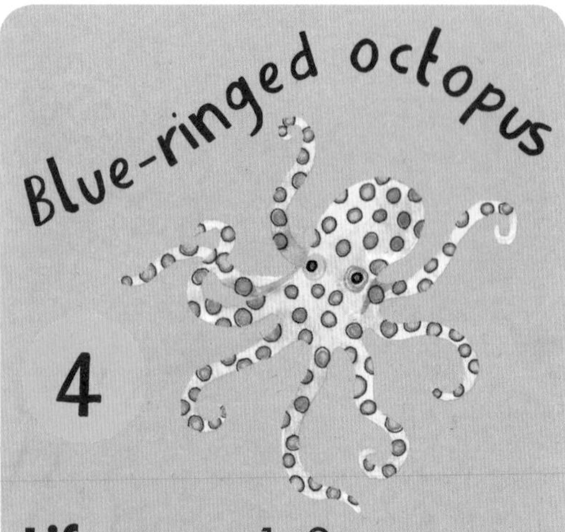

Lifespan: 1–2 years
Diet: Crabs and molluscs
Skill: Its blue rings flash as a warning when it is threatened.

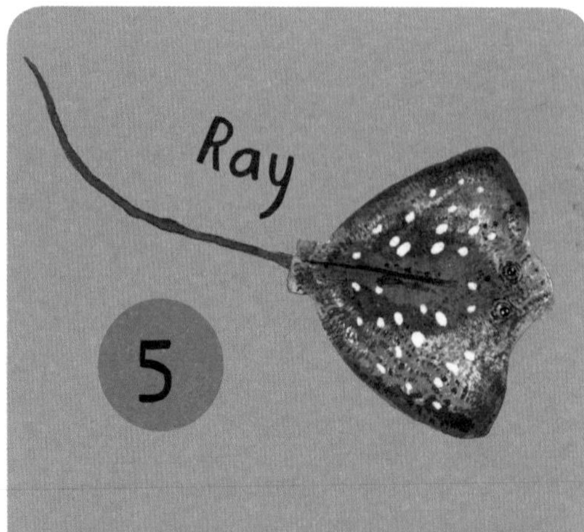

Lifespan: 20 years
Diet: Zooplankton
Skill: It has its skin cleaned by smaller fish which pick off parasites.

Lifespan: Up to 4 years
Diet: Shrimp and plankton
Skill: The males give birth to live babies.

1
2
3
4
5
6

Polar

These animals live in the polar regions. Penguins only live in Antarctica. Colour them in!

1

Giant squid

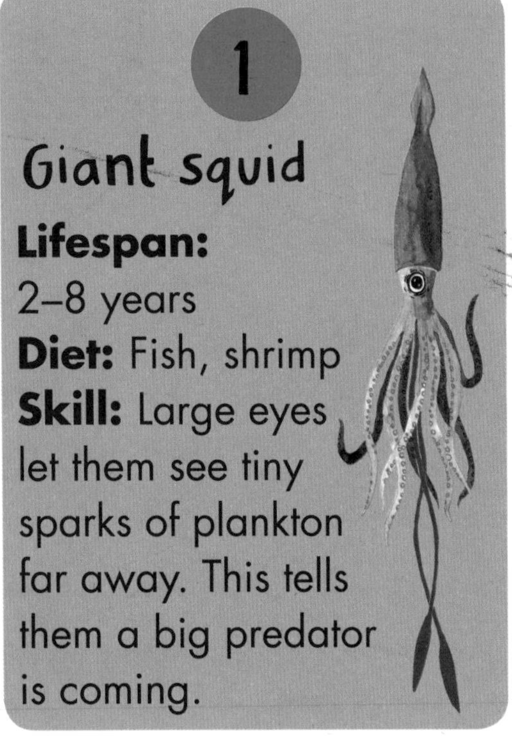

Lifespan: 2–8 years
Diet: Fish, shrimp
Skill: Large eyes let them see tiny sparks of plankton far away. This tells them a big predator is coming.

2

Emperor penguin

Lifespan: 20 years
Diet: Fish, krill and squid
Skill: It can survive snow storms and cold weather.

3

Narwhal

Lifespan: 25–30 years
Diet: Fish, shrimp and squid
Skill: The males fight each other with their long tusks.

Adelie penguin

4

Lifespan: 11–20 years
Diet: Fish, krill and squid
Skill: They line their nests with rocks they have collected.

5

Blue whale

Lifespan: Up to 90 years
Diet: Krill
Skill: They sing across oceans to other whales.

6

Seal

Lifespan: 25–35 years
Diet: Fish and squid
Skill: Seal babies can swim soon after they are born.

1
2
3
4
5
6

Savannah

These animals live on the African savannah. Colour them in!

Lifespan: 15 years
Diet: Insects, eggs and dead rodents
Skill: It digs for food with its long, curved bill.

Lifespan: 12–16 years
Diet: Zebra and wildebeest
Skill: It has excellent eyesight and can see well in the dark.

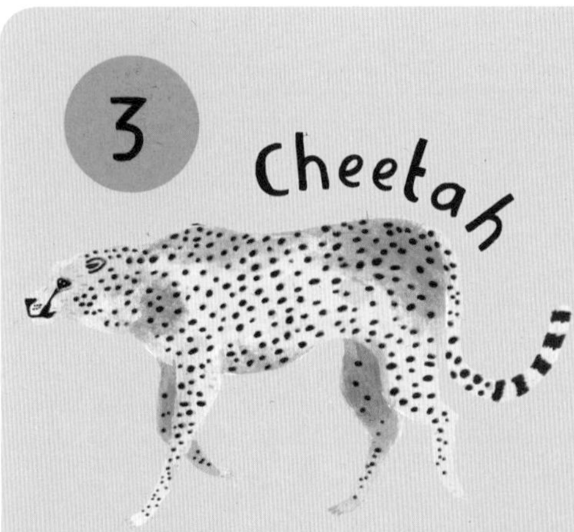

Lifespan: 10–12 years
Diet: Gazelle-sized mammals
Skill: It is the fastest land mammal in the world.

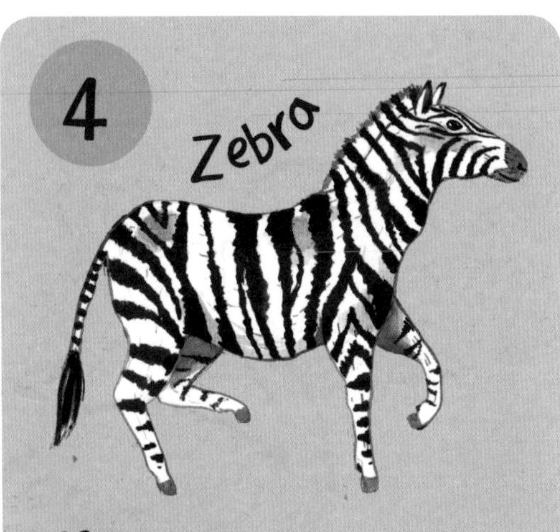

Lifespan: 25 years
Diet: Shrubs and leaves
Skill: They can gallop for a long time to help them escape predators.

Lifespan: 25 years
Diet: Acacia leaves
Skill: They strip leaves from tall, thorny trees.

Lifespan: 40 years
Diet: Brine shrimp and algae
Skill: They can stand on one leg, maybe to help them save energy.

1
2
3
4
5
6

Learn More!

Forest

Forests are the lungs of our planet. They clean the air that we breathe. They are tightly packed with trees, providing homes to many animals.

Desert

Desert temperatures soar by day and get very cold at night. There isn't much water either, so the animals and plants that live here are well-adapted to survive.

Jungle

Tropical forests are hot and humid all year round. They are home to a rich variety of plants and animals that thrive in this climate.

Mountains

Animals here are used to living on high slopes. It gets very cold and hard to breathe at the highest points of a mountain range.

Savannah

The African savannah is very dry – but some grasses and trees do grow. Animals like zebra graze on these plants and then become food for predators such as big cats.

Polar

The animals that live here have to survive in the coldest conditions in the world. Not many plants or animals live on the polar ice. Most of them rely on the sea for food.

Ocean

Ocean covers most of our planet. From coral reefs to deep sea beds, it gives a home to many creatures. Animals who live here are well-adapted to life in the ocean – they may have tails or fins that help them swim.

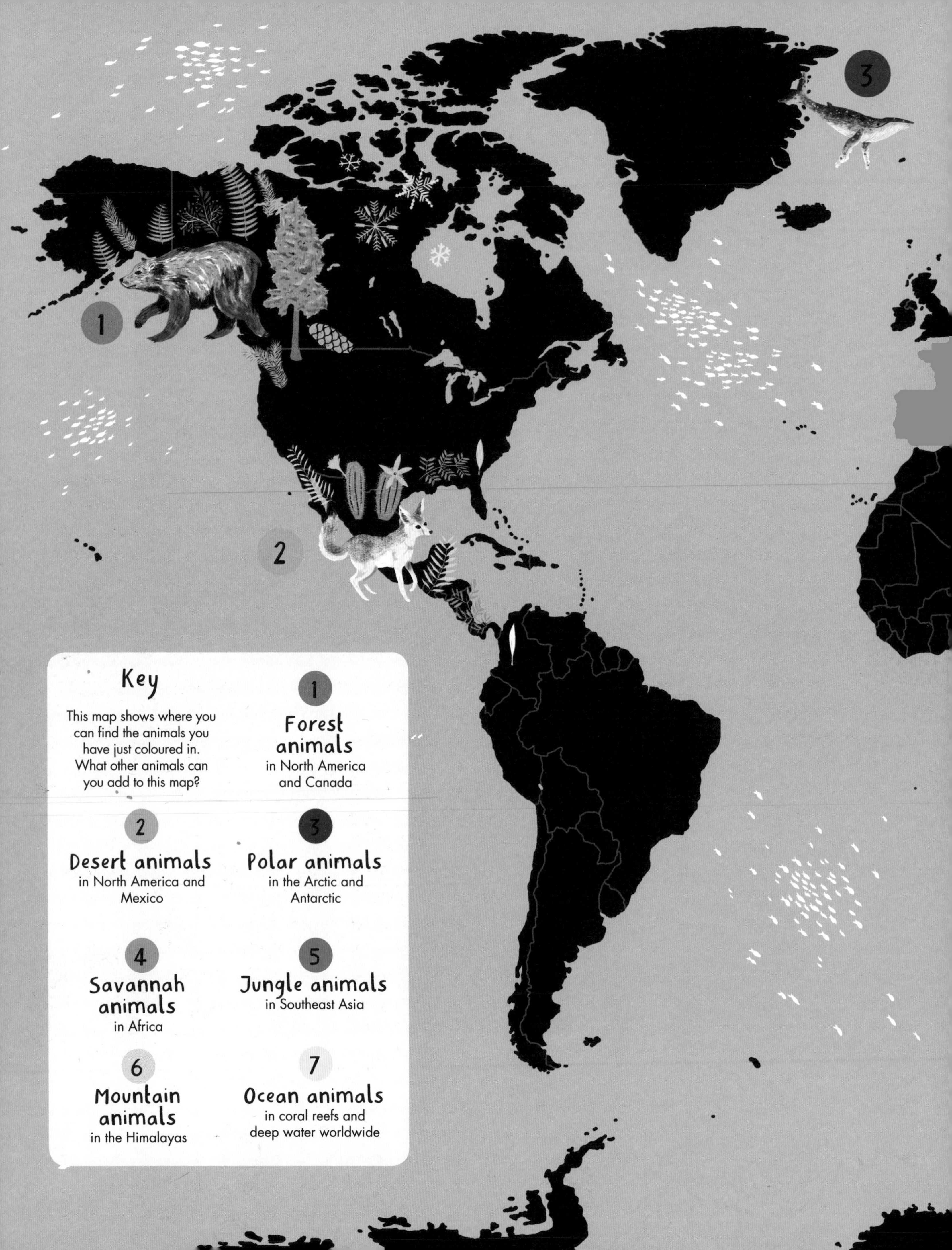
1
2
3
Key
This map shows where you can find the animals you have just coloured in. What other animals can you add to this map?
1
Forest animals
in North America and Canada
2
Desert animals
in North America and Mexico
3
Polar animals
in the Arctic and Antarctic
4
Savannah animals
in Africa
5
Jungle animals
in Southeast Asia
6
Mountain animals
in the Himalayas
7
Ocean animals
in coral reefs and deep water worldwide

6
5
4
7
3

Also available in the series

Fuzzy Dinosaurs and Prehistoric Creatures by Papio Press

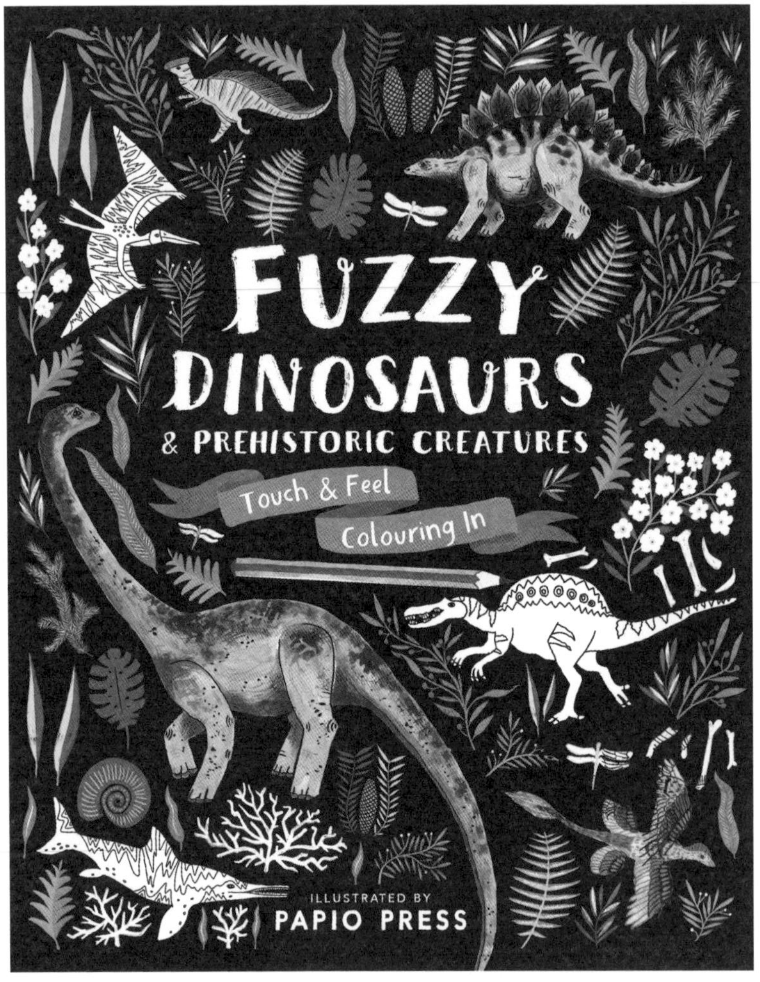

ISBN 978-1-78603-164-8

Explore the prehistoric world as you colour in each touch-and-feel chart. Meet the plant-eaters, the meat-eaters, the sea-dwellers and the high-fliers. Featuring art of the world's best-loved and most spectacular dinosaurs to colour in. With facts for every prehistoric creature to keep you entertained.

BEHIND THE MASK

THE SECRETS OF HOLLYWOOD'S MONSTER MAKERS

BEHIND THE MASK: THE SECRETS OF HOLLYWOOD'S MONSTER MAKERS
ISBN 1 85286 488 5

Published by
Titan Books Ltd
42-44 Dolben Street
London SE1 0UP

First Titan edition August 1994
10 9 8 7 6 5 4 3 2 1

British Library Cataloguing-in-Publication Data. A catalogue record for this book is available from the British Library.

Picture credits:

Allied Lane Pringle Productions, Amblin Entertainment, AIP, Avco Embassy Pictures, Elaine Baker, Rick Baker, Lois Burwell, Carolco Pictures Inc, John Carpenter, Columbia, Joe Dante, Entertainment, Jim Eustermann, Filmplan International, Hollywood Book and Poster, Steve Johnson, Larco, Dino de Laurentiis, Lee Rich Productions, Larry Lurin, Manifesto Film Sales, MGM, New Line, New World Pictures, Paramount, Robert Picardo, Polygram, Zade Rosenthal, Lorey Sebastian, Dick Smith, Tomorrow, Twentieth Century Fox, United Artists, Universal City Studios, Bob Villard, Warner Bros, Stan Winston

Acknowledgements

We would like to extend our very special thanks to all those who gave so freely of their time to be interviewed: (in alphabetical order) Rick Baker, John Carpenter, Joe Dante, Steve Johnson, John Landis, Robert Picardo, Dick Smith, Stan Winston. Thanks are also due to Steven Spielberg, Alan Jones, everybody at *Empire,* Mark Kermode, Steve Jones, Kim Newman, Magrit Hedgcock, Fiona Hedgcock, Cliff Wallace, Brenda Lonergan, Dave Elsey, everybody at Creature Effects, Tony Timpone, Ian Hedgecock, Lois Burwell, Rupert Murdoch, Tara Crichito, Kim Verros, Bob Villard, Jennifer Sebree, Karin Costa, Crash McCreery and everybody at the Stan Winston Studio, Matt Britton, Diane Duncan and Joe Fordham. Awards for their enthusiasm, patience and understanding go to David Barraclough, Katy Wild and Chris Teather. And finally, for services above and beyond the call of duty, a special spectacularly big round of applause to Murray Hedgcock and Jo Bond, without whom etc...

To Mum and Dad, with much love. MS

To my parents for their love and support, and to all the artists who have inspired me. AH

Printed and bound by in Great Britain by Stephens and George Ltd, Merthyr Industrial Estate, Dowlais, Merthyr Tydfil.

BEHIND THE MASK

THE SECRETS OF HOLLYWOOD'S MONSTER MAKERS

MARK SALISBURY & ALAN HEDGCOCK

Foreword by John Carpenter

TITAN BOOKS

Contents

Foreword

The mask has always been with us...

Humans gathered around fires to ward off evil, death, the unknown — and at the firelight, the mask was there. In the literature of man, his poetry, painting, on the stage, the screen, the walls of caves, the image of the mask hovers like a dream, a phantom...

The mask swims with our projected fantasies, our darkest personal records of dread...

I first encountered the mask in 1953. I was four years old. My mother took me to see *It Came from Outer Space*, Jack Arnold's science fiction visitation epic, and when the Xenomorph slowly lurched its way out of the darkness of the cave into the light, I went ballistic. My four year-old brain was fried. Neurons fused. I was hooked.

It took a huge eyeball surrounded by swollen, oval-shaped flesh and Christmas tree tinsel. And it didn't walk like a man — it appeared to be "kinda crawlin'" as the old woman said two years later in *The Quatermass Experiment*. Regardless, I was absolutely convinced I was looking at a monster from outer space.

Twenty-nine years after *It Came from Outer Space*, I directed *The Thing*, based upon John W. Campbell's novella *Who Goes There?* Throughout my stint at film school at the University of Southern California and the early beginnings of my writing and directing career in the movie business, I was told that the best way to scare an audience was through 'indirection' — that is, "keep the damn monster in the shadows and half-light so we don't get a good look at it".

Baloney! I remember what it was like to be four years old and think I just saw a monster from outer space come out of the shadows into the light. One of the reasons I wanted to remake *The Thing from Another World* was to convince everyone over four that they were, in fact, seeing that hideous beast!

The Thing was made in 1982, and by that time the technology of special make-up effects had evolved to the point where I could take that ol' xenomorphic shape-shifting, human-body-rearranging nightmare out of the closet of shadows and fast-cutting, and into the light.

During the first audience preview of *The Thing*, a woman jumped to her feet during the dog sequence, dashed to the restroom and threw up. Upon hearing this news, the head of production at Universal turned to me and said, "We've got a hit!"

Special make-up effects have become one of the world's newest art forms since Linda Blair's head rotated and spat green vomit in *The Exorcist*. Dick Smith began the modern era — and, with bladders pumping, cables twisting, levers pulling, goo flowing, Rick Baker and Rob Bottin brought it to its highest moments. No longer did a big space

Below: *John Carpenter on the set of* In the Mouth of Madness.

Left: *Director Carpenter at work.*

Above: *Make-up artist Rob Bottin as Captain Blake in John Carpenter's* The Fog.

monster get rolled out on a dolly by a stagehand — now these creatures could change, grow, crack open, roar, sit up, talk, devour, creep, boogaloo or just about anything else in the world you could think up for them to do — right in front of your eyes. Special make-up effects became hyper-real, surrealistic — visceral art — claw and slime so textured and believable I'm certain Luis Buñuel would smile in absurdist admiration. They hit the psychosis deep inside American culture: the obsession with physical perfection and beauty, the repulsion with human sexuality.

Before Dick Smith, make-up was a very different ballgame. Jack Pierce created the classic make-up for Boris Karloff in James Whale's *Frankenstein*, but it was the actor who primarily animated the creature's character. Paul Blaisdell made the monsters in *The She-Creature*, *It Conquered the World* and *The Day the World Ended*, but the rubber suits were more fun than frightening.

Les Bowie created the world's first slop monster in Val Guest's *The Quatermass Experiment*, but inserted the eye of an octopus into the footage in order to pull the audience into the last vestiges of humanity left in the thing on the scaffolding in Westminster Abbey. Phil Leakey created Christopher Lee's make-up in Terence Fisher's *The Curse of Frankenstein*, Eiji Tsuburaya came up with the rubber suit and producer Tomoyuki Tanaka played the part of Gojira — or Godzilla as he is known in Western culture — who, along with King Kong and the Frankenstein monster, remains one the most popular movie monsters.

But the rubber was rubber. It was fun, but it was rubber.

It's hard now to comprehend the kind of impact *The Exorcist* had upon its initial release. To put it bluntly, the audience went apeshit. An unusually conservative, religious horror picture, *The Exorcist* added the adolescent girl to those twin terrors of physical beauty and sex, and wrapped it all up with the Devil — the ultimate evil in the ultimate mask. Two years later Nature, in the form of a huge rubber shark, sent audiences gibbering in *Jaws*, but the fear wasn't as personal. *The Exorcist* showed us what would happen if evil got into us. Predicated on a belief in God, the movie demonstrated Ol' Scratch and his antics, and the audience lost its collective bowel control.

The impact of special make-up effects upon audience and industry is unquestionable. Mainstream action pictures deftly incorporated techniques from horror films, including the use of special make-up. To what extent computer generated effects will supplant rubber and bladders remains to be seen.

This book celebrates the twenty Golden Years of the Mask, and shows us where and how the Beasties are given life to romp and stomp upon our psyches.

So, if you dare, gentle readers, turn the pages...

Listen! There's something moving out there. Look! Just beyond the firelight, swimming in our imagination, the Mask is coming this way, and it means to make you scream.

John Carpenter
Los Angeles, May 1993

Introduction

Ever since an eighteen year-old Mary Shelley put pen to paper and thought up the story of a medical student named Victor Frankenstein with the dream of creating a perfect human and who, inadvertently, gave birth to a monster instead, public appetites have shown an insatiable desire for tales of monsters and their makers. But while Shelley's monster was just the figment of a young girl's imagination, there are those working today whose job it is to give life to the monstrous, to the inanimate, to the creatures that readily haunt our dreams and lurk around the fringes of our imagination, who turn Jekyll into Hyde, make the unreal real, the dead walk. These are today's Frankensteins, today's monster makers. They are the men behind the mask.

As John Carpenter states in his foreword, men were being transformed into cinematic monsters long before Dick Smith turned the cherubic

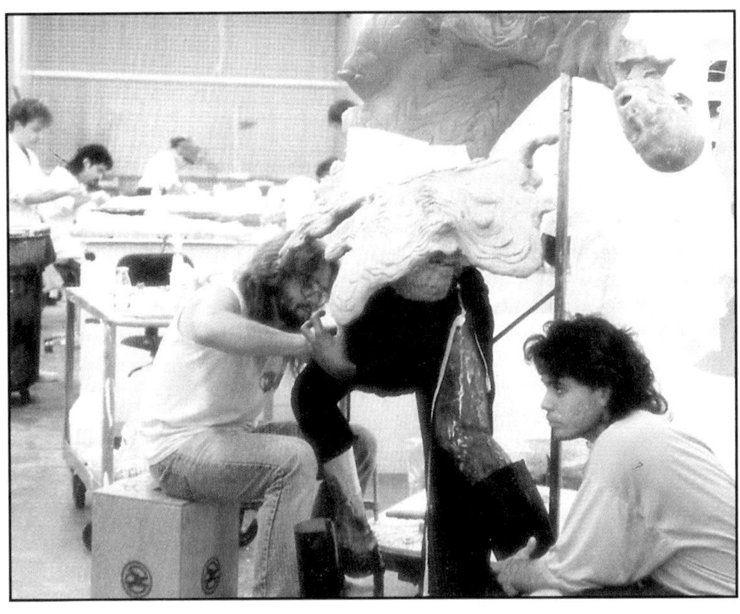

Above: *Sculpting the Pretzel Man for* Terminator 2: Judgment Day. ***Left:*** *The Dean of Make-up Effects, Dick Smith.*

Right: *Rick Baker with his* Greystoke *ape sculptures.* ***Opposite top:*** *Baker's test make-up for Jack in* An American Werewolf in London, *before Griffin Dunne was cast.* ***Opposite bottom:*** *Rob Bottin, Joe Dante and crew on the set of* Twilight Zone: The Movie.

twelve year-old Linda Blair into a vomit-spewing demon in William Friedkin's *The Exorcist* (1973). Lon Chaney made himself up as *The Hunchback of Notre Dame* (1923) and *Phantom of the Opera* (1925), Jack Pierce pioneered the bolt through the neck look for Boris Karloff as the monster in *Frankenstein* (1931), Jack Dawn gave life to L. Frank Baum's Tin Man, Lion and Scarecrow in *The Wizard of Oz* (1939), while John Chambers won an honorary Oscar for his simian designs in *Planet of the Apes* (1968). But it was Smith, whose career began in television in the forties and who turned Dustin Hoffman into a 121 year-old frontiersman in *Little Big Man* (1970) and Marlon Brando into an ageing mafia don in *The Godfather* (1971), who combined the techniques of prosthetic make-up with those of special effects (mechanics, puppetry) to create something new, pioneering the art of special make-up effects as it is practised today. An art that can readily turn a girl into a demon, a man into a werewolf, or a visiting extra-terrestrial into just about anything technology and imagination can muster.

Behind the Mask is neither a comprehensive history of make-up effects nor a technical manual that will turn you into the next Dick Smith, Stan Winston or Rick Baker. Instead, it is a celebration of the art and careers of those who, we feel, in the twenty years since *The Exorcist* have shown themselves to be the leading exponents of their craft. Dick Smith for his pioneering techniques and generosity of spirit — *The Exorcist, Altered States* (1980), *The Hunger* (1983); Rick Baker for his perfectionism — *An American Werewolf in London* (1981), *Greystoke: The Legend of Tarzan Lord of the Apes* (1984), *Harry and the Hendersons* (1987); Rob Bottin for his surreal imagination — *The Thing* (1982), *Legend* (1985), *Explorers* (1985); Stan Winston for the scale and quality of his work — *The Terminator* (1984), *Aliens* (1986), *Predator* (1987), *Terminator 2: Judgment Day* (1991), *Jurassic Park* (1993); Steve Johnson for his strong design ethic — *Ghostbusters* (1984), *The Abyss* (1989), *Freaked* (1993). All but one are Oscar winners, and all are equally deserving of books of their own. But why these five in particular? The answer is as much a personal one as one judged on merit. Tom Savini, Greg Cannom, Chris Walas, Tony Gardner, Kevin Yager and the Burmans are all considerable figures in the field, but our chosen five not only had a most profound influence on their art, but on us. They are the five whose work most inspired, thrilled, scared or just plain amazed us.

When David Naughton transmogrified from man into lycanthrope in John Landis' *An American Werewolf in London,* it wasn't just a revelation in terms of make-up effects. We sat in the cinema, our mouths agape, our eyes not quite comprehending what was happening up there on the screen. As 'Blue Moon' played on the soundtrack and Naughton changed from man into wolf, it was so totally unlike any werewolf transformation we had ever seen. This wasn't Oliver Reed in Hammer's *Curse of the Werewolf* (1961) or Lon Chaney Jr in Universal's *The Wolf Man* (1941). There were no lap dissolves, no cutaways, no funny filters. No. Naughton's skin rippled. His limbs stretched. Bones cracked. Hair forced its way through his flesh. *A man turned into a werewolf. Right in front of our eyes.*

When, in Carpenter's *The Thing*, someone comments, "You've got to be fucking kidding!", it was a response that seemed to come not only from the actor up there on screen but from the lips of every member of the audience. Nothing on earth could have prepared us for the sight of a heart attack victim's chest giving way during cardiac massage to reveal a set of gnashing teeth, or a head that slowly becomes detached from its owner's body, sprouts spider legs, eyes on stalks, and then scuttles across the room.

But these modern monster makers are more than freak show hosts or purveyors of gore. Smith finally won the Oscar he had long deserved not for any outlandish creature transformation, but for his outstanding character make-up in Milos Forman's Mozart biopic *Amadeus* (1984); Baker realised a dream of a lifetime and created apes virtually indistinguishable from the real thing in *Greystoke: The Legend of Tarzan Lord of the Apes* and *Gorillas in the Mist* (1988); Bottin succeeded in bringing Tex Avery cartoons to life in *Twilight Zone: The Movie* (1983); Johnson proved that ghosts could be funny as well as terrifying in *Ghostbusters*; Winston's work on both *Terminators* is as memorable, if not more so, than Arnie's "I'll be back!", while the dinosaurs of *Jurassic Park* speak for themselves.

But what of the future? With computer generated imagery (CGI) so refined as to produce a wholly convincing herd of galloping dinosaurs or a liquid metal Terminator at the touch of several buttons, and computer morphing popping up in virtually every other TV show, pop promo or commercial, many within the industry fear for the continued existence of traditional make-up effects. But in *The Abyss*, *Terminator 2* and *Jurassic Park*, computer effects were all supplemented by rubber monsters. As Stan Winston says, "There will always be *the art.*" And that is what this book is all about, the art and imagination Behind The Mask.

Magazines such as *Fangoria*, *Cinefantastique* and *Cinefex* have been here before, and we owe them our thanks, not just as a valuable source of reference material but also for their inspiration, enthusiasm, knowledge and guidance whilst we were growing up. Al Taylor and Sue Roy mined similar territory with their book, *Making a Monster*, but they wrote of a time before *The Howling* and *The Thing*, before Rick Baker was awarded the first competitive Oscar for make-up for *An American Werewolf in London*. This is a book for the *Fangoria* generation, for those who grew up wanting to be Rick Baker, Rob Bottin, Stan Winston, Steve Johnson or Dick Smith. This is a book dedicated to the time when rubber ruled... ■

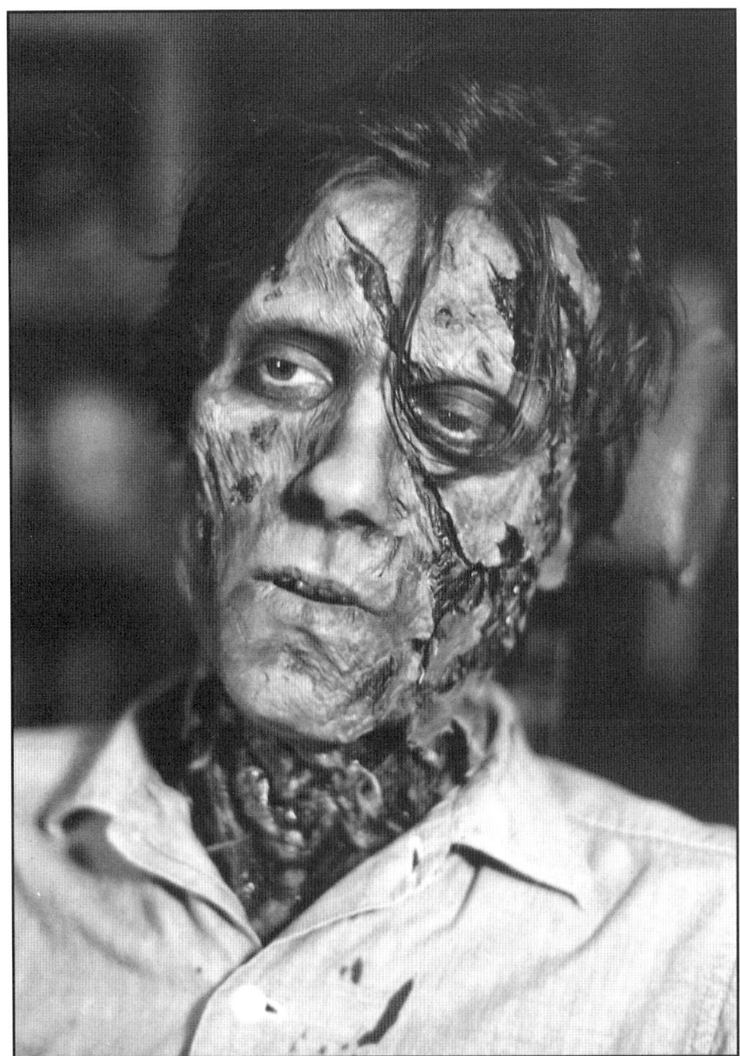

Chapter One

Vomit-spewing demons and elderly priests

Dick Smith and his pioneering work on The Exorcist

The godfather of special make-up effects was born Richard Emmerson Smith in Larchmont, New York on 26 June 1922. While he would later be revered for his artistry, as a child he initially showed little promise in that direction: "I was not a good artist. I was the sort of boy who was always envious of someone else in the class who was a great cartoonist. I didn't draw well. I still can't. I *can* draw, but it's an effort." Smith's creative side, however, began to reveal itself when he started drawing moustaches on the faces of people in his textbooks: "I discovered if I took a pencil eraser, I could erase part of the half-tone pictures of historical characters. Using both my ability to take away and to add, I turned these pictures into horrible things, monsters or something crazy, just as a matter of amusement. I guess my fascination with changing faces just kind of happened in those high school days."

When Smith was seventeen he saw *The*

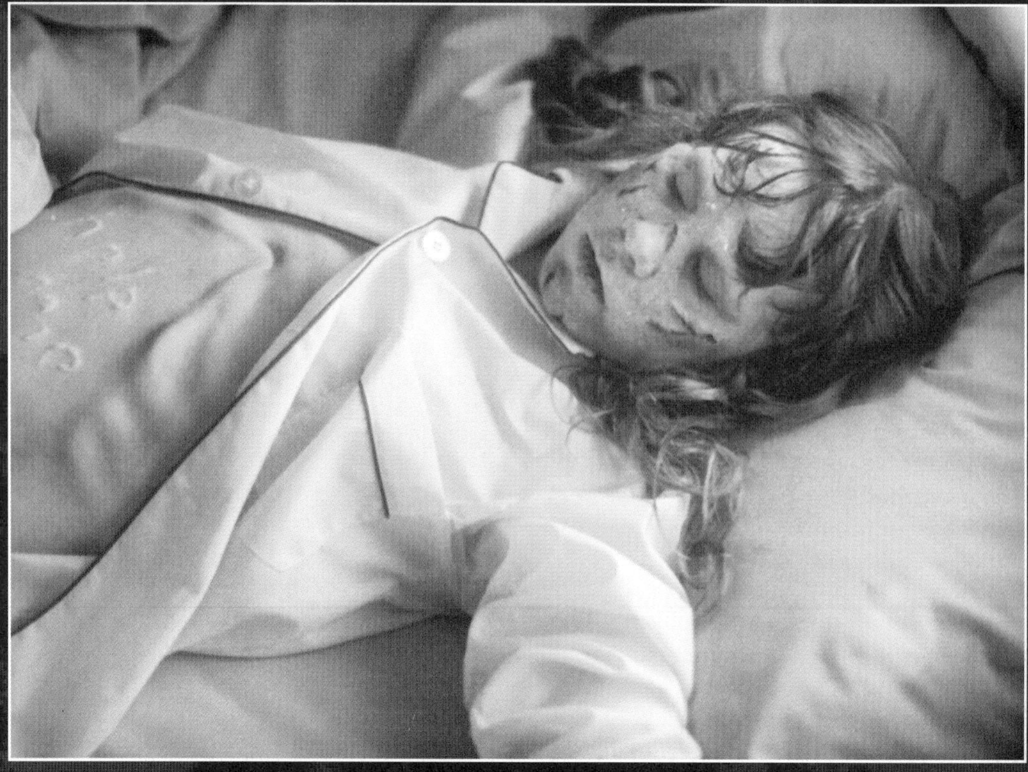

Opposite: *Linda Blair sporting a foam-latex chest and demonic appliances.*
Left: *Not Linda Blair again, but a very convincing dummy, used primarily for the infamous sequence in which her head turns through 360 degrees.*

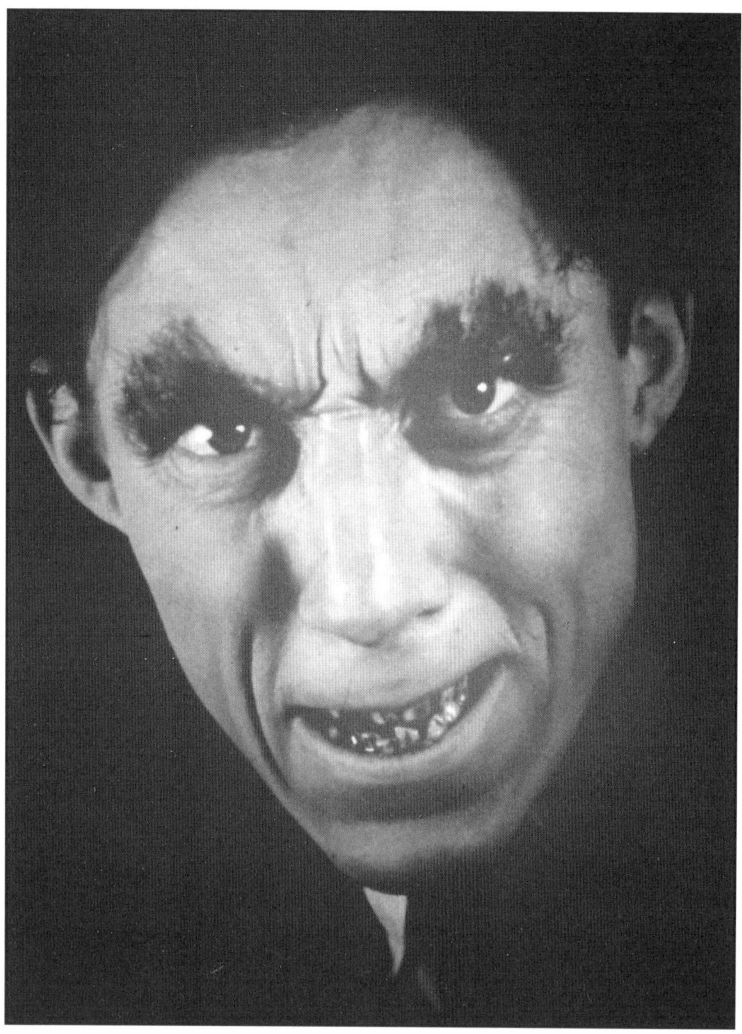

Above: *The nineteen year-old Dick Smith as Mr Hyde.* **Right:** *Smith as Quasimodo, based on the make-up created by Perc Westmore.*

Hunchback of Notre Dame (1939), starring Charles Laughton as Victor Hugo's deformed bell-ringer. He had previously seen a picture of Laughton in Perc Westmore's make-up in *Life* magazine and had been truly fascinated by it: "There was a big review and many pictures, including the only one printed for many, many years of the Laughton make-up. It was a tiny little thing, about the size of two postage stamps, and it absolutely fascinated me. Here was something really artistically and marvellously creative."

Smith's early efforts at make-up amounted to little more than brushing his hair and pencilling on a moustache to make himself look like Hitler. It wasn't until he was at Yale University (initially studying engineering before switching to pre-med with the intention of becoming a dentist) that his interest in make-up took root when, aged nineteen, he came across Ivard Straus' *Paint, Powder and Make-up* in the university's bookshop: "I can clearly remember finding the book, it was on sale, fifty per cent off. On the cover was a picture of the author made up as a Neanderthal man, it was pretty grotesque, so I grabbed the thing. It was very crude, but to me it was magical."

Using the book as a guide, Smith began to experiment with the basics of theatrical make-up (grease paint, nose putty, spirit gum), transforming himself into those cinematic monsters he had admired as a teenager. He began with Mr Hyde and progressed onto Laughton's Quasimodo, the Phantom of the Opera, the Wolf Man and the Frankenstein Monster, the latter based on the design that his make-up idol Jack Pierce had perfected for Karloff. "I discovered when I got into make-up I could become someone else," remembers Smith, who would run around campus in make-up and costume frightening his friends. "It was a lark, but it had an amazing emotional effect on me. I was stepping out of myself into someone else's skin. That's what hooked me. The make-up itself is one thing, but the actual things that happened to me wearing the make-up were as much of a hook. To be someone else, to act out feelings that perhaps as a shy person I could not express, was very therapeutic."

The advent of World War Two caused Smith to re-evaluate his planned career: "The war and the prospect of not coming back in one piece makes you think what you want out of life. And I came to the conclusion that I didn't want to go back to dental school." Instead of returning to Yale, Smith decided to pursue make-up professionally. Trying his luck in Hollywood, Smith sent samples of his work to the heads of make-up at several studios with little success, receiving a number of encouraging letters but no offers of

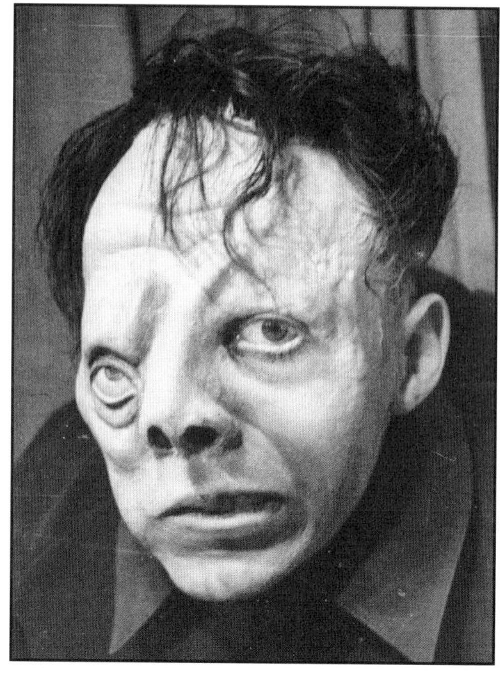

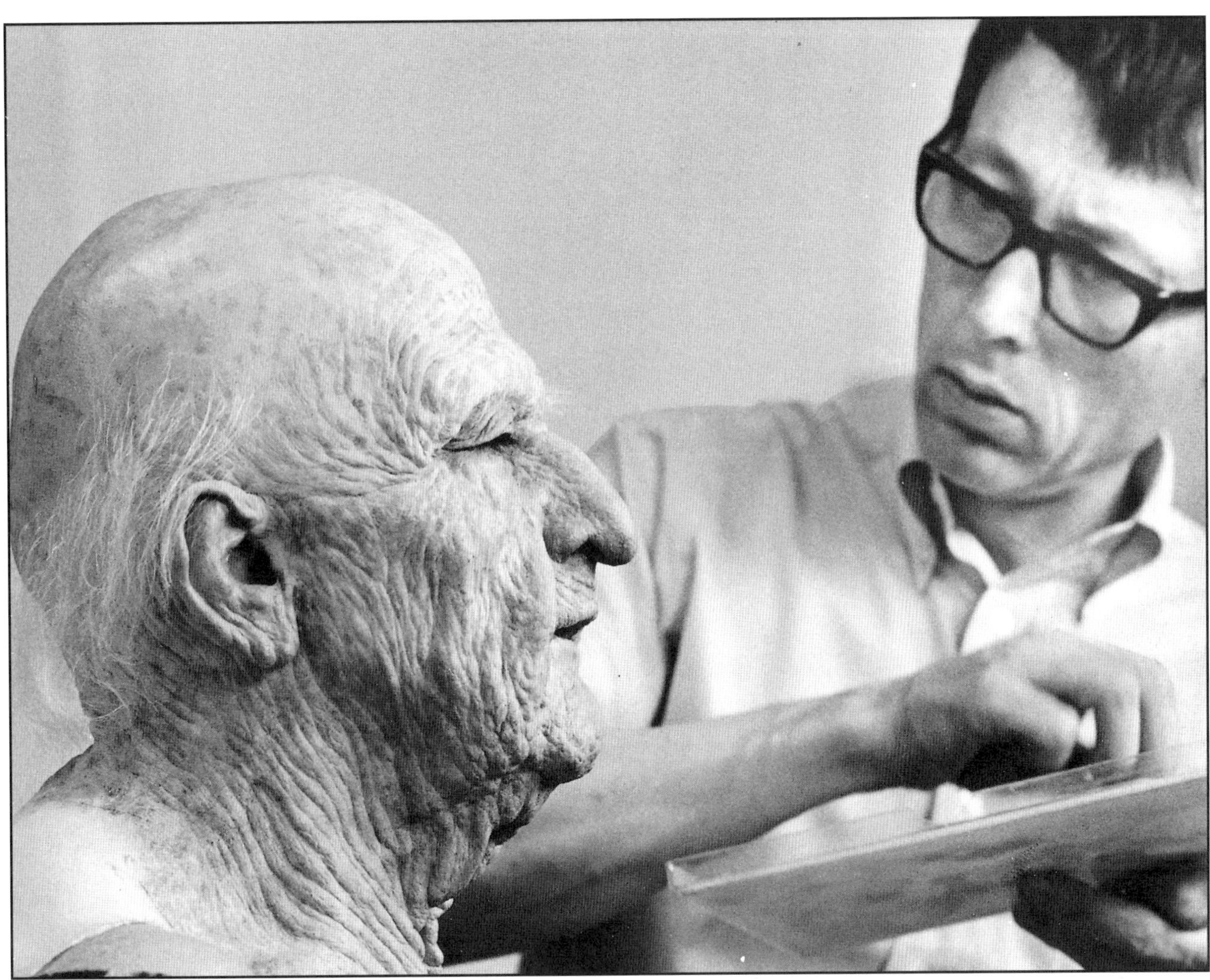

Above: *Dustin Hoffman, then just thirty-three, underneath Smith's seminal make-up.*

work. Smith's father, a book publisher and head of the New York Film Censorship Board, suggested he try television, then in its infancy. Thus in June 1945, aged twenty-three, Smith started on a six-month contract at NBC for $50 a week. He was TV's first staff make-up man.

"Television was my school. Because what I had learned from reading a few books, practising and making myself up as monsters was nothing. I had to learn as I went along, and quickly, because in five years I had a department of twenty make-up artists working for me. We did everything — all kinds of ageing character and period make-ups. It was non-stop, it was very exciting and very creative, and I not only gained experience, but also self-confidence. And I felt that, miracle of miracles, I was actually becoming a pretty good make-up artist. And I never expected I would."

Since TV dramas were then transmitted live, Smith was often called upon to touch up and sometimes even apply whole make-ups during commercial breaks. It was during this time that Smith learnt the basics of old age make-up which was to later prove his speciality: "Live television was an extraordinary thing. There was no testing, no preparation. You never had time to perfect anything."

Smith's six-month trial at NBC turned into a fourteen-year stint. He made the move into features in 1959, with James B. Clark's *Misty*, a film memorable only for a freak accident in which he snagged his wedding ring on a wooden railing while jumping off a truck. (The wound turned gangrenous, necessitating the amputation of the ring finger on his left hand.) Returning to TV for a further two years with David Susskind's Talent Associates, Smith's next feature was *Requiem for a Heavyweight* (1962). In 1969, he made up Dustin Hoffman as the seedy lowlife Ratso Rizzo opposite Jon Voight's cowpoke stud in John Schlesinger's Oscar-winning *Midnight Cowboy*. Smith reteamed with Hoffman a year later on Arthur Penn's *Little Big Man* (1970), in which he turned the then thirty-three year-old actor into the film's 121 year-old title character Jack Crabbe, a Western pioneer who reminisces of his time as an adopted Indian

Right: *Linda Blair in the throes of demonic possession, unaware she was making film history.*
Below right: *Linda Blair's dummy double indulging in some head-turning activity.*

and sole white survivor of Custer's last stand. An elaborate make-up that covered Hoffman's entire head and took some five hours to apply, it, together with his next project, Francis Coppola's *The Godfather* (1972), thrust Smith into the Hollywood spotlight and earned him the reputation as the master of old age make-up. The top box office success of its year and an Oscar winner for Best Film, *The Godfather* brought Smith much attention. However, it was his next job, *The Exorcist* (1973), which changed both the course of make-up and his life.

Based on the best-selling novel by William Peter Blatty, *The Exorcist* was ground-breaking not just in terms of its blending of prosthetic make-up with special effects but also for its unrelenting intensity and sheer explicitness. While director George Romero had wrenched horror from its Gothic trappings five years earlier with the seminal *Night of the Living Dead* (1968), Blatty's story of a twelve year-old girl (Linda Blair) possessed by a demon and transformed into an obscenity and vomit-spewing abomination proved to have an even bigger impact, scaring the bejesus out of audiences around the world on its way to becoming the biggest horror film of all time. Brought onto the project five months before shooting began by director William Friedkin and producer

OLD AGE MAKE-UP

The first stage in creating an old age make-up, as with most prosthetics, is to life-cast the actor's features. Dental alginate is applied over the face and head of the actor being cast and allowed to set. It is this layer that captures every detail on the face, right down to the individual skin-pores. This fragile alginate layer is strengthened by the addition of strips of plaster bandage which, when hard to the touch, can be removed from the actor. The negative mould that this produces is filled with plaster, or in some cases plastaline, an oil based clay similar to children's modelling material. This leaves you with a plaster duplicate of the subject onto which the various aged features — wrinkles, folds and jowls — are sculpted.

Traditionally, at this stage, the whole face would be moulded in plaster and a one-piece mask produced. But, following Smith's lead on *Little Big Man*, where, for the first time, the features were divided into separate appliances which overlapped, it became standard to create one mould for the nose, one for the upper lip, one for the lower lip and chin, and so on.

Each separate piece is then moulded in plaster or, as is now more often the case, in fibreglass or epoxy. The end result is a two-piece mould for each part of the face, an eye-bag or forehead. Into these moulds, foam-latex is poured or injected using a custom-made syringe and baked in an oven for several hours. When removed from the mould, the foam piece has to be trimmed of any excess and any air bubbles or seams filled.

Finally, each piece is carefully glued to the actor's face using a medical adhesive, having been pre-painted with pax paint to save time, or coloured after application with rubber grease paint. ■

Above: *F. Murray Abraham as Antonio Salieri in* Amadeus, *Smith's Oscar-winning make-up.* ***Left:*** *Smith's 'invisible' effect for* The Exorcist. *Max Von Sydow as Father Merrin.*

Above and opposite: *Linda Blair in Smith's test make-ups.*

Blatty, Smith's immediate task was to turn the apple-cheeked, wholesome-looking Blair into the demonic Regan.

"Arriving at Linda Blair's make-up was an endless nightmare," explains Smith. "I did about five different versions, all quite extreme at first. Then I boiled it down to one that seemed workable, and perfected that." Unfortunately, when filmed, Friedkin considered the make-up was still too extreme and Smith had to start again: "I went crazy trying to come up with a better solution. We went through another five make-up tests and we still didn't have it. Then we finally put together kind of an amalgam of a little bit of this and a little bit of that. Friedkin always wanted scratches (*on Regan's face*) because in the exorcism that Blatty based his original story on, the young boy had self-inflicted wounds." Smith was averse to the idea because he disliked horror make-ups that relied solely on blood and gore for their effect: "What I was able to do was salvage the treatment I had worked on before, which blocked out her eyebrows and gave her frontal bones which were somewhat skull-like. That, together with the painting around them, made her eyes more menacing. Every cut, scar and wound was designed to make her face more asymmetrical. They were placed very carefully. Her lips were distorted by appliances to make them look twisted."

Although conceptually challenging, Blair's demon make-up wasn't anywhere near as technically innovative as some of the other effects Smith was called upon to design. The one which typifies his ground-breaking blending of make-up and special effects occurs during the scene where the words 'Help me' appear on Linda Blair's stomach while she's sleeping. To create the effect, Smith toyed with a number of different ideas — including using either a false rubber stomach with rigid letters pressing up through the skin or inflatable letters — but abandoned them as being impractical. His solution was to construct a foam latex appliance of Blair's chest and stomach, and then, using a chemical liquid which causes foam to swell, paint the words 'Help me' on it. A heat gun was then pointed at the appliance and the fluid evaporated rapidly, an effect which when filmed in reverse gave the illusion of the words rising. "I loved the 'Help me' thing, but I was upset with Billy (*Friedkin*) because he cut away in the middle of the sequence," remembers Smith. "It looked like they cutaway for a reason, to do something with the make-up. But it did go from zero to full effect in one take."

For the infamous scene in which Regan's head turns through 360 degrees, Smith created a life-

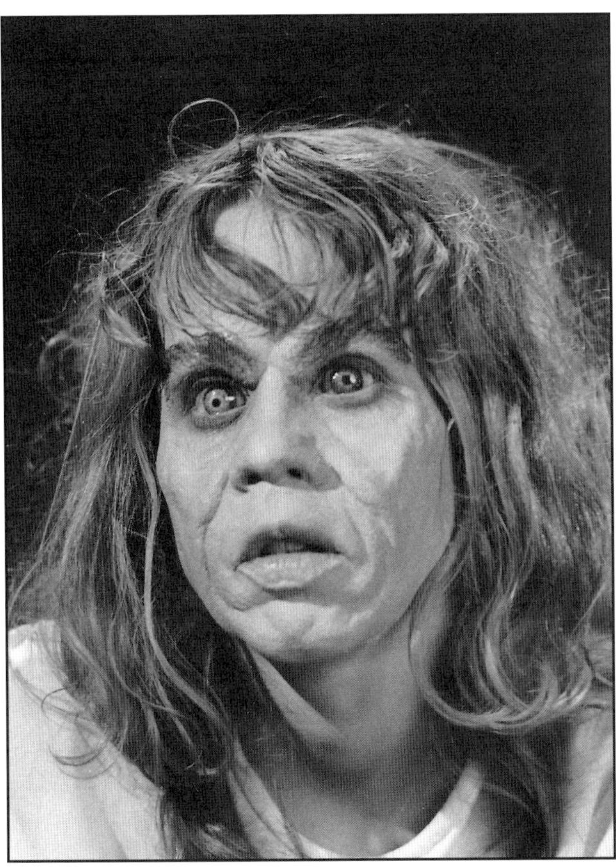

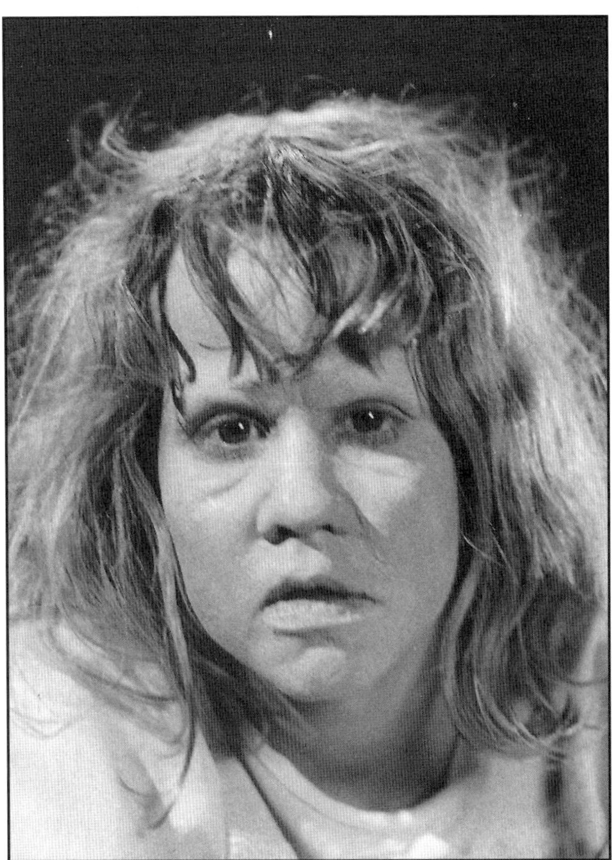

size mechanical dummy of Blair which took the make-up artist and his young assistant, Rick Baker, six weeks to build, with the pair having to cast every part of Blair's body. To make the eyes look from left to right, special effects co-ordinator Marcel Vercoutere installed a radio control device, as well as a hand-crank to rotate the head which was operated from under the bed. Vercoutere also ran a tube up the inside of the dummy and into the mouth to pump steam through. When the steam came in to contact with the set's refrigerated air, the dummy appeared to be breathing. "They cut from Linda, to the dummy's head rotating, picked it up when the dummy stopped, going back to Linda with her hair twisted around her neck and a shoulder appliance on her front, to make it look like her head was on backwards when she delivered the lines," says Smith. "It was a wonderful effect, greatly enhanced by the editing."

The Exorcist was the first film to make use of the so-called bladder effect, a technique that was to later form the basis of the spectacular transformations in *Altered States* (1980) and *The Howling* (1981) among others. "In the script it said, 'Her throat blew up like a bullfrog,'" explains Smith of the genesis of the effect in which a balloon is inflated underneath a prosthetic appliance. "I took a single sheet of condom rubber, glued it in a circle, glued the edges all around on her neck and ran a tube under one edge. And then I made a very, very thin foam latex neck piece which I stretched over it."

Arguably Smith's most difficult challenge was the scene in which Regan spews a projectile stream of green vomit at Jason Miller's Father Karras. At first assuming the scene would be filmed from the side, Smith came up with a tube going into the off-camera side of Blair's mouth, hidden by a prosthetic appliance. Friedkin, however, insisted that the shot be filmed head-on, which Smith initially felt would be impossible. The solution he came up with involved running two flat plastic tubes along the cheeks of stunt double Eileen Dietz (who stood in for Blair for the effect) and into her mouth, coming together at a nozzle. Foam appliances were then glued over the tubes, so when her face was seen from the front it appeared normal. Vercoutere hooked a pump up to the tubes and on cue fed green pea soup through them. Originally Friedkin had wanted the vomit to spray out, but during the editing decided it should appear more direct, virtually dumping the effect as filmed and replacing it with a shot of Blair lunging forward with an optically inserted stream of vomit spewing from her

Above: *Test make-up approved and filmed, although ultimately dropped.* **Right:** *Blair's make-up as seen in the finished film.*

mouth. The Smith/Dietz combination effect can, however, *still* be seen in the finished film — albeit *very* briefly — for a few seconds after Miller is first splattered, and again much later in the film when Regan lies on her side and vomits into Father Merrin's purple stole during the exorcism sequence.

But perhaps Smith's most convincing creation is, ironically, the one that even today goes largely unnoticed. In the role of the septuagenarian exorcist Merrin, Friedkin cast the forty-four year-old Swedish actor, Max Von Sydow, presenting Smith with the task of ageing him thirty years. A masterly age make-up which took three hours to apply, it was a combination of subtle appliances and old age stipple and the result of much experimentation, with Friedkin insisting on three complete screen tests before he was satisfied with how Von Sydow looked.

"*The Exorcist* was a painful film to work on in a sense because the stress was enormous," admits Smith. "Billy Friedkin I love, but he was a real tough guy on that. There were times when we almost came to blows, and I did literally quit at one point over an argument with him. But we finished it, and we've been good friends ever since. I knew I was doing things that hadn't been done before. But throughout my career I've constantly made improvements in technologies so that it didn't seem to me that I was working in a landmark, just that I was working in something that was very challenging and very difficult and required all my ingenuity. It combined all the key things I never had on any other film: the ageing on Max, the demonic make-ups on Linda, and then it had the special make-up effects, which, of course, I now recognise as being the birth of that field."

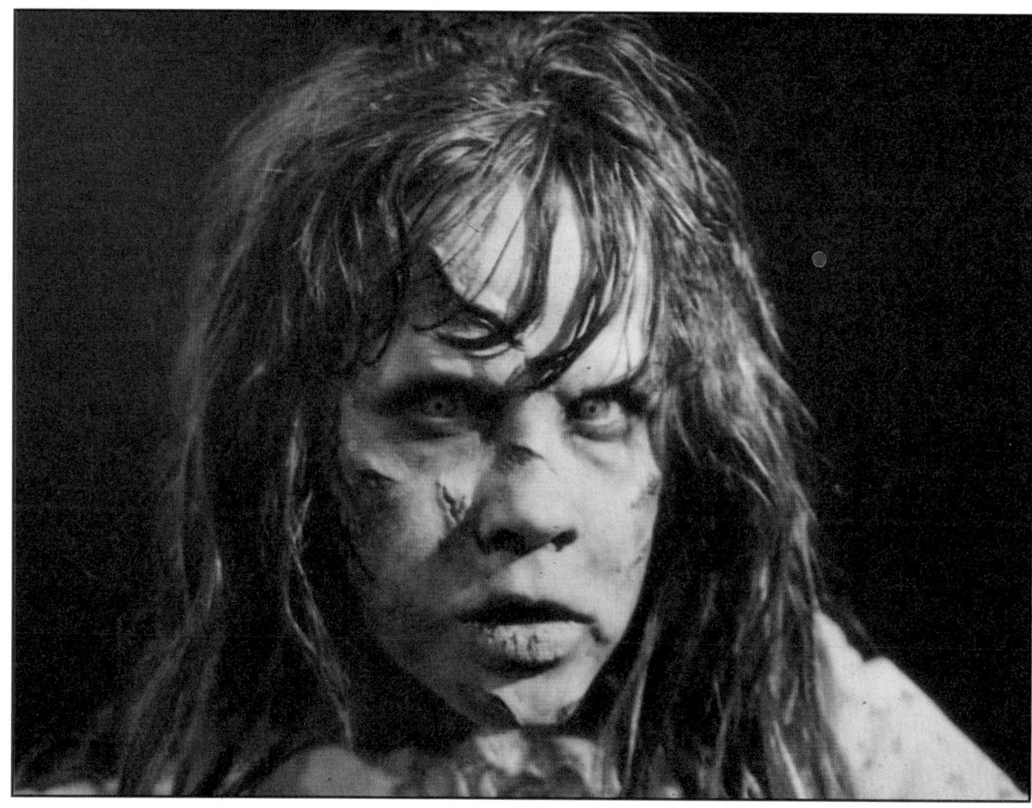

***Above:** Smith testing the 'help me' chest effect.*

Dick Smith's contribution to make-up effects far exceeds his pioneering use of materials and techniques in *The Exorcist*. In the years since that groundbreaking film, Smith's knowledge and love for his craft has inspired two generations of artists, while his willingness to teach and demonstrate his methods has provided both an injection of enthusiasm and promoted an interest in make-up. Smith has always found time to share his hard-won knowledge, remaining open about his discoveries, a direct consequence of the secrecy and closed shop mentality he encountered when he began in the business: "When I started it was all very secretive, and that always angered me. People would hang on to secrets and not share. I have a missionary instinct I suppose. The only way I can use it is by helping other make-up artists. It's the way I make friends; people like me if I help them, of course. There is also a certain amount of ego in it. I used to consider whether I should keep a certain thing secret in the early television days. But then I would say to myself, 'What do I need it for? I'm only going to think of something better next year, it will be out of date. I don't need to be secretive.'"

Smith's first effort to share his knowledge with a wider audience was through his *Monster Make-up Handbook*. Published in 1965 through *Famous Monsters of Filmland* magazine, Smith's handbook proved a godsend to countless aspiring make-up artists throughout the world, opening up a realm of possibilities with its host of basic make-up techniques, formulas and information regarding the availability of materials: "Because of the success of *Famous Monsters*, there was a lot of interest in monsters among younger people. And it, of course, reminded me of the fun I'd had when I'd played around with make-up as a young man at Yale. The knowledge that it's been an inspiration to so many people like Rick (*Baker*) is wonderful. People constantly tell me that it's what started them off, so I'm very proud of it."

One make-up artist indebted to Smith's handbook is Steve Johnson, who first discovered it as a teenager and who years later worked with Smith on David Cronenberg's *Videodrome* (1982): "I was looking at the new edition of the *Monster Make-up Handbook* just this morning and all these memories came flooding back — I've got the whole thing memorised. I was standing in my workshop with thirty guys wandering around making all this cool stuff, and I thought, 'What if I *never* had this book?'"

Now semi-retired, Smith has still found ways

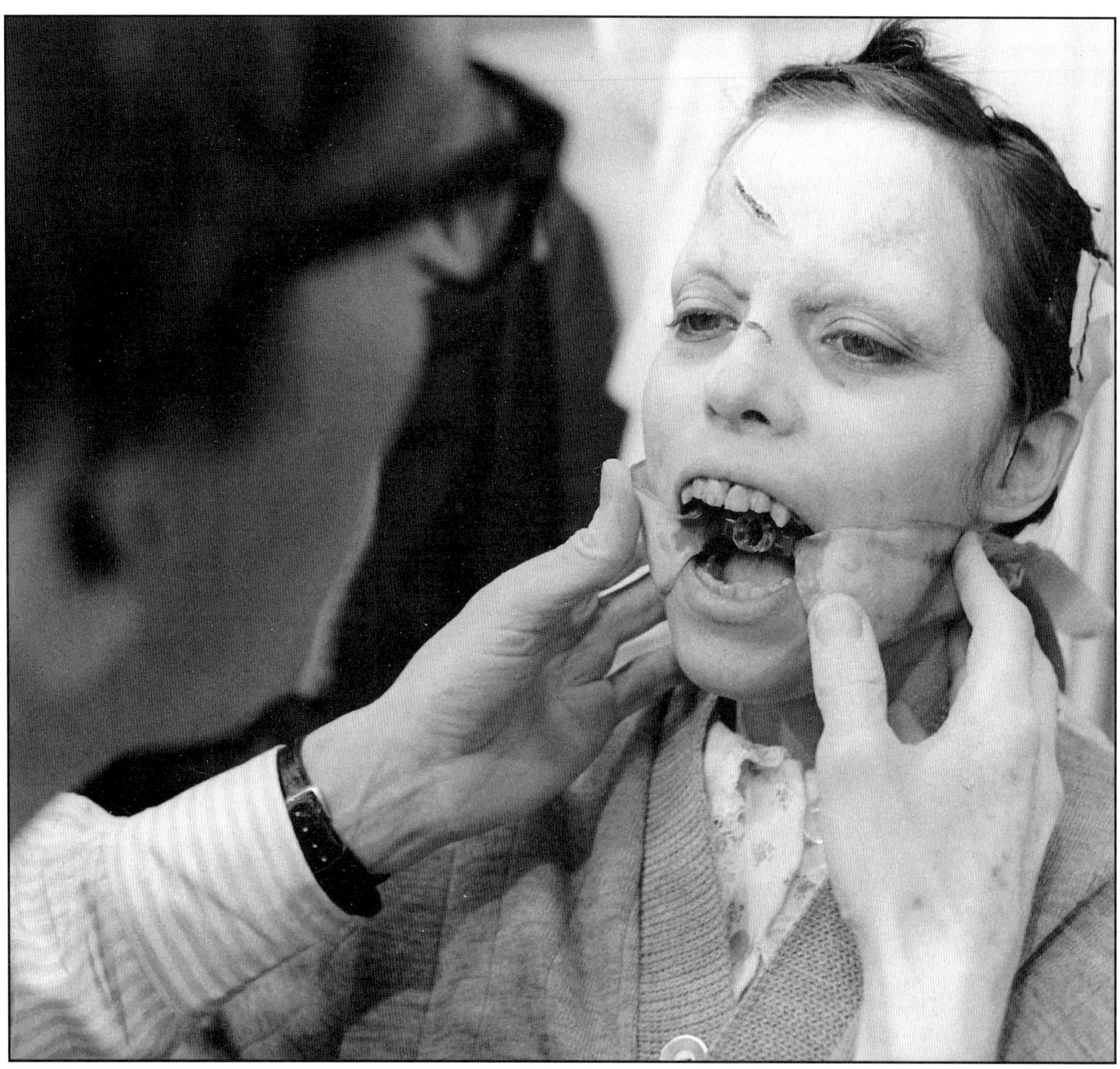

Above: *Smith fitting the vomit spray device to Eileen Dietz, Blair's acting/make-up double.*

to impart his legendary knowledge through his Advanced Professional Make-up Course, a correspondence course he began in 1985 and which is the Bible for today's make-up artists, presenting all the formulas, techniques and step-by-step instructions invented and collated by Smith over the years. Having won the Academy Award for Make-up with *Amadeus* (1984), Smith originally intended to put his life's work down in book form, but decided a course would better serve his purpose: "It has worked out wonderfully. It took me almost two years to write, and now it helps in my retirement. I update it when I can, and so I still have this connection to the profession that I love. As long as I live, I'm going to do that."

Smith's influence on today's make-up effects artists is unquestionable. "Dick Smith was definitely the guy that started the make-up effects revolution," says Baker. "Dick's the make-up god."

"Dick Smith is inspiring in so many ways," says Stan Winston. "Far beyond what a terrific artist he is, and how exceptional his work always was. As a human being, he is an amazing inspiration. He's not the youngest one of us now, but he's always there, always wanting to know what's going on, learning from it, giving his information. The man never had any secrets. For me, he was an idol. I remember when I saw the Dustin Hoffman make-up in *Little Big Man*, it was like 'God!' And I still look at it and go, 'Wow! How terrific!' He is a terrific artist who cares so much about his craft. I can't say enough as to how he has influenced me, my work and hopefully my work ethic. Dick Smith is the best."

Steve Johnson agrees: "Dick Smith *is* the best. He's the only person who's ever taken responsibility for this business. By compiling his correspondence course, he has locked down all these formulas, a lifetime of incredible research that would have gone out the door. I know I'm not the kind of person to sit back, to formulate something, to do a bunch of tests with some chemical. I don't think Rick Baker's that way; Stan's not that way; none of us are. I don't even write down a formula. But Dick's put everything in that book and none of us can ever be thankful enough. It's all there; we refer to it practically every day. Plus he's a genuinely nice man. And I hope to God that I still love make-up as much as he does when I'm his age. He really loves it more than anyone I've ever met."

Smith modestly suggests that his generosity is not purely altruistic: "I've always felt sharing information was a good thing to do, just from the standpoint of common sense. As it's turned out, I have benefited from my own policy, because in this last era I couldn't possibly know all the things that have been developed by this wonderful younger generation of artists. But I can call them up and say, 'How did you do that?' And now I can learn from them. If I had not been instrumental in bringing about this freedom of exchange of information, this brotherhood, I wouldn't be getting that help. So that's a good thing."

So how does Smith feel about being called the make-up god?

"I think it's a certain amount of exaggeration, but I have stopped arguing with people about it. I only explain by saying that I really didn't have any confidence in my creative abilities when I started. And even years afterwards, though I accepted that I was a good make-up artist, the idea never entered my head that someday I would be referred to as the 'Legendary Dick Smith'. I mean, that is an incredible thing to happen to you. It's an enormous joy, of course. Hell, it's better than winning any Academy Award." ■

Below: *Eileen Dietz in full throw, an effect cut from the final film.*

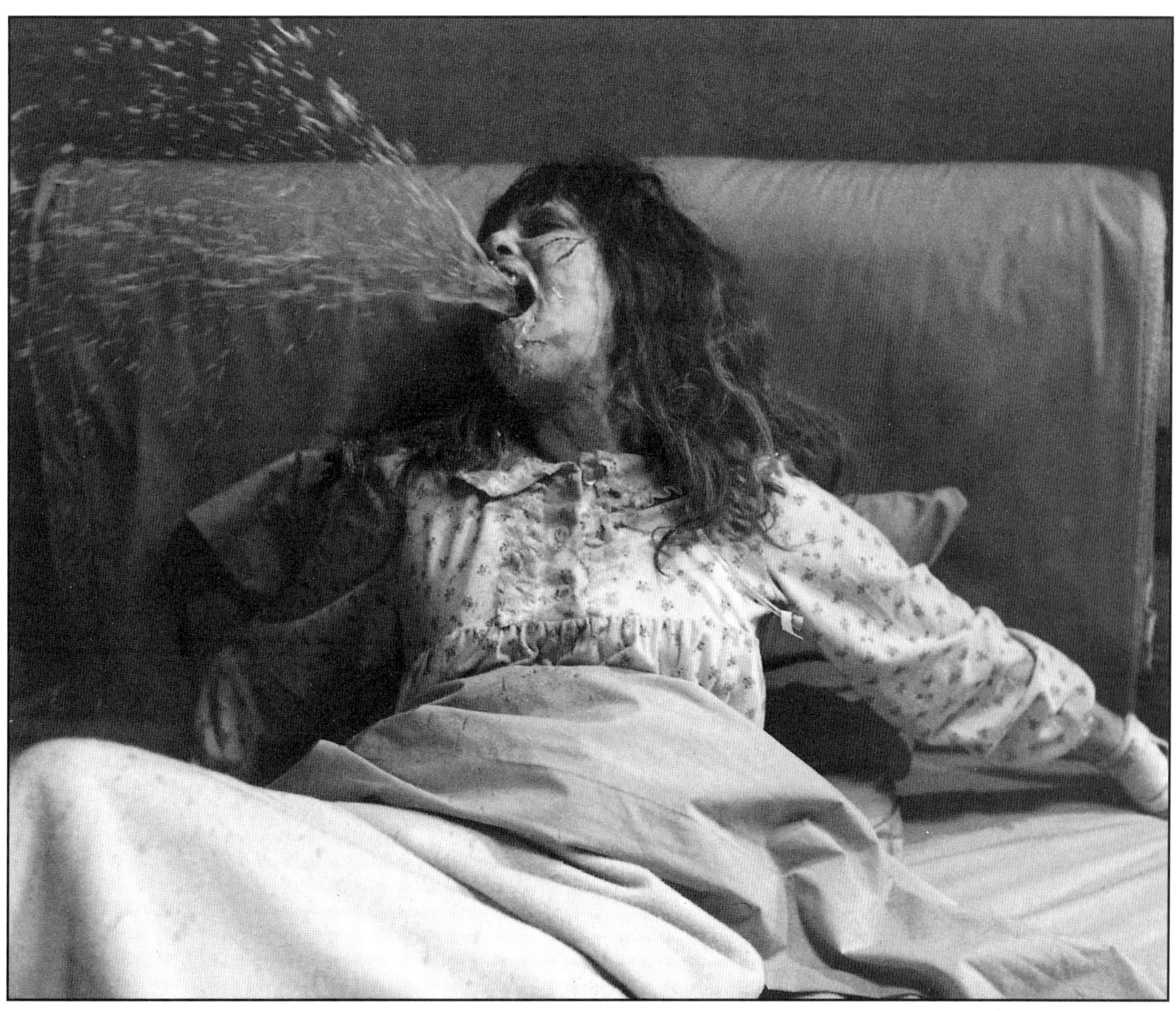

Chapter Two

From boy to monster

The early career of Rick Baker

Dick Smith's assistant on *The Exorcist* was Rick Baker, then aged twenty-one, who had already provided the title monsters for a couple of low-budget films: Harry Essex's laughable *Octaman* (1971) and John Landis' début feature *Schlock* (1972). Baker had first met Smith on a trip to New York in the late sixties after corresponding with him for several years: "Dick called up and said, 'I'm kind of in a bind here, would you be interested in coming to New York and working on this movie with me?' I packed my bags and went right away. It was like a dream come true. I lived in a room in his house and worked in his famous little lab in the basement and got to watch Dick sculpt and apply stuff. And it was *The Exorcist*, a *cool* movie." Baker worked on the film for five months, flying to Iraq to assist Smith in applying Von Sydow's make-up. "We laugh about it now," says Baker, "but at the time it was a huge picture. There were so many things in it; it was a case of 'How are we ever going to do this much stuff?' But it's like a piece of cake compared with what's been done since."

A shy child, Baker had wanted to be a make-up artist since he was ten when he saw an article in *Famous Monsters of Filmland* entitled 'Boy Into Monster', which showed a make-up artist at work. Realising for the first time that movie monsters

Opposite: *Baker's painting of Boris Karloff as the Monster from James Whale's* Frankenstein. ***Left:*** *For the 1976 remake of* King Kong, *Baker both sculpted and played the title creature.*

Right: *An early Quasimodo make-up, at the sculpting stage.* ***Far right:*** *Rick Baker, age eleven, in a pie dough make-up.* ***Below:*** *Rob Bottin's drawing of Lon Chaney Sr that so impressed Rick Baker.*

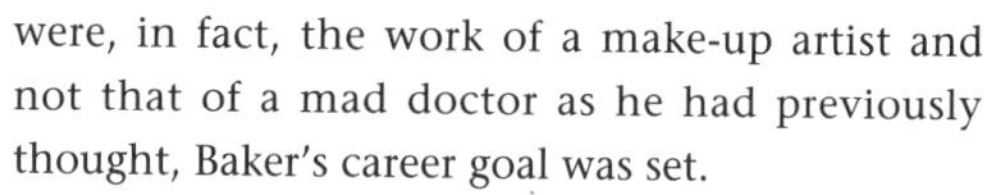

were, in fact, the work of a make-up artist and not that of a mad doctor as he had previously thought, Baker's career goal was set.

Baker began with simple paint make-ups on himself and his friends in Covina, California,

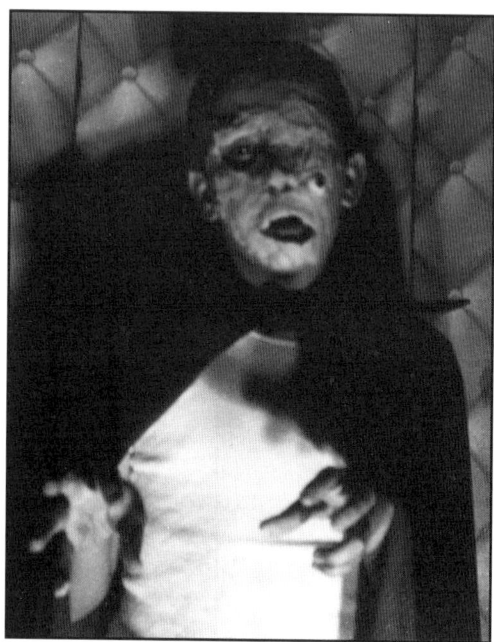

later experimenting with pie dough sculpted onto his face into suitably grotesque shapes, before progressing to mask-making with the help of his father. His first effort was a copy of Christopher Lee's monster make-up from Hammer's *The Curse of Frankenstein* (1957): "When I was a little kid I didn't go out and play army with the other kids or play with little cars, I made and drew monsters. I grew up in a lower-middle class neighbourhood where guys I knew were committing major crimes. Making rubber monsters kept me out of trouble."

Baker, however, admits to a brief "blood and guts" phase, making up his friends with third-degree burns, gashes, even bullet wounds, before he learned the error of his bloody ways: "I found out if I did a gory thing I could fool somebody with it, people thought it was real. Then I decided that wasn't necessarily a good thing. Supposing you give somebody a heart attack or somebody runs out in the street and gets run over."

Looking for an equally realistic alternative to his gory effects, Baker hit upon the idea of making a gorilla suit, which still indulged his passion for monsters but was less likely to get him into trouble. It was during a trip to the newly opened Universal Studios Tour for his thirteenth birthday that Baker came across a display featuring the work of make-up artist Bob Burns, who had made

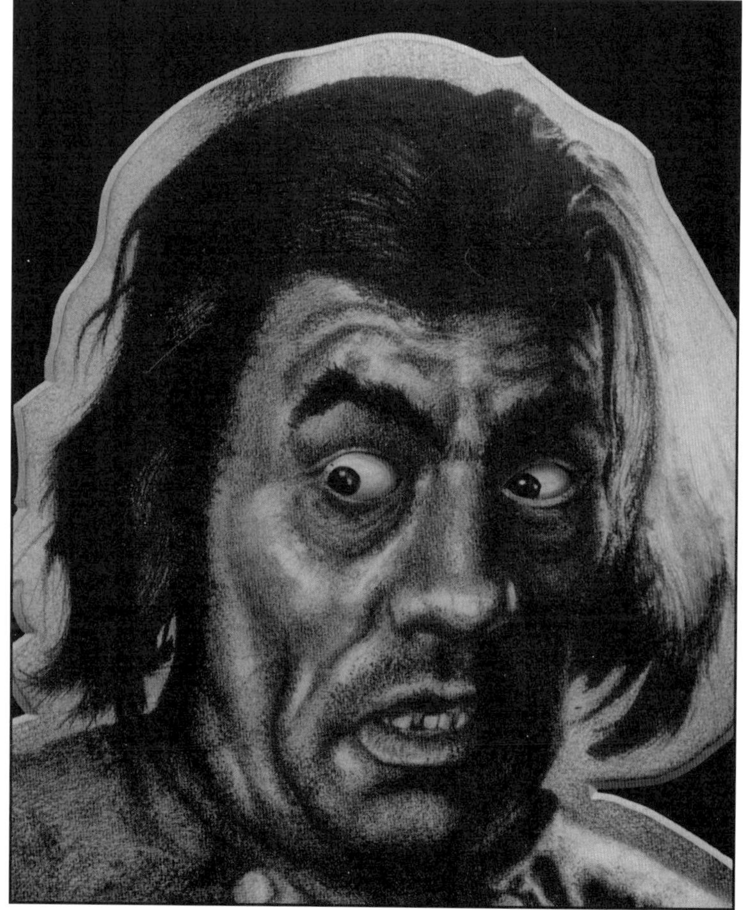

the gorilla suit for Ray Dennis Steckler's *Rat Pfink a Boo Boo* (1965), a film which had helped fuel the young Baker's enthusiasm for apes. Through a contact at Los Angeles-based mask makers Don Post, Baker obtained Burns' telephone number, and the pair soon became firm friends. "He had a gorilla suit. It wasn't very good but it was pretty cool," Baker remembers, "and I started looking at gorilla movies more and more. It was like a quest, I wanted to make a real gorilla suit, some day I wanted to make something real."

A year later Baker came across a copy of Dick Smith's *Monster Make-up Handbook*, which was to prove a revelation. Baker bought two copies and set to work, eventually plucking up the courage to write to his hero, whose work he had admired through the pages of *Famous Monsters*: "I was a fan of all the make-up artists, but there was one guy whose work was so much better than everybody else's — that was Dick. Before I even knew his name I would just see pictures and think, 'This is great, who did this?' And every time it was Dick Smith, Dick Smith, Dick Smith. *I idolised him.*"

When Baker had what he considered to be presentable samples of his work, he sent them along

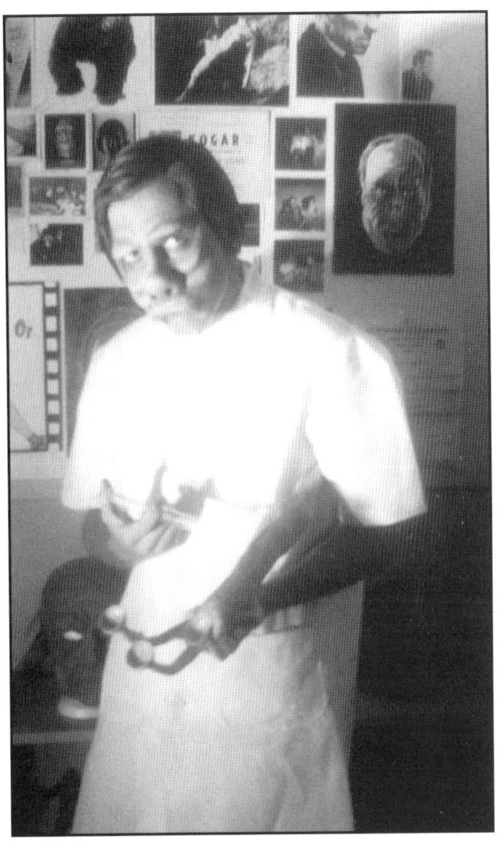

Left: The Outer Limits *episode 'The Eye of the Beholder' was the inspiration for this early Baker make-up.*
Below: *Baker age sixteen with a display of his monstrous creations.*

with a letter to his hero, and was delighted to receive a swift reply — an encouraging letter, including an invitation to visit Smith's East Coast workshop. It wasn't until Baker had graduated from high school that he was able to take up Smith's offer, when he and his parents took a trip to New York to visit relatives. Thinking he was in for little more than a brief tour of Smith's workshop, Baker was surprised to be given a notebook on entry: "I spent a day with him where he told me everything in the world about make-up. It was right at the beginning of the trip and I wanted to go home immediately. I didn't care about meeting the rest of the relatives. Dick told me all this stuff I couldn't wait to try. He took me under his wing and taught me a lot."

"Rick sent me a bunch of pictures," remembers Smith. "Here was a kid, still in his late teens, unlike any I had seen up to that time, who was already a fantastic sculptor and mask-maker. He did work that was equal to ninety-nine per cent of existing make-up artists. It was extraordinary. I was just so delighted to see this young kid doing this fantastic work, I just had to meet him."

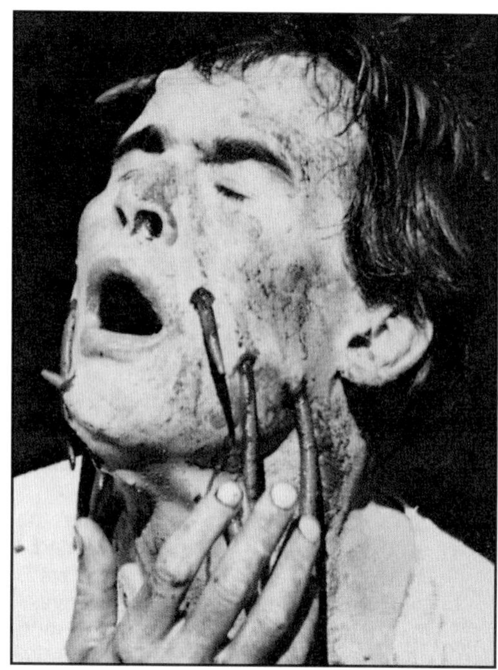

***Right:** Rick Baker's worm-face make-up for* Squirm. ***Opposite:** The baby monster constructed for Larry Cohen's* It's Alive! ***Below:** A lifelong fan of Jack Pierce's work from* Frankenstein, *Baker poses with a full-size figure of the Monster he made for his home dungeon!*

Following Baker's visit, the pair corresponded regularly, with Smith arranging for his young protégé to sit in as an observer on *Little Big Man*, culminating in Smith's call to assist him on *The Exorcist*.

It was while Baker was working on *The Exorcist* that he was approached by director Larry Cohen to create the monstrous baby for his latest film *It's Alive!* (1974). Creator of the sixties TV series *The Invaders* and later director of cult favourites *Q — The Winged Serpent* (1982) and *The Stuff* (1985), Cohen had previously called upon Baker to provide a number of bloody corpse make-ups for the obscure comedy *Bone* (1972), having seen the ape suit Baker had made for *Schlock*. Cohen initially had his own concepts for the fanged baby, which included Baker fabricating a monster suit for either a cat or, even more bizarrely, a pair of chickens to wear. Luckily for the chickens, Baker talked Cohen out of it, suggesting they use a stop motion model or a mechanical puppet instead. In the end, a lack of time and Cohen's assurance that the baby would only be seen briefly resulted in Baker creating a foam figure with a simple wire skeleton. Such was Cohen's enthusiasm for it, however, that he decided the baby should act, so Baker constructed a mask and a set of claw-handed gloves for a puppeteer to wear. Cohen, now with a moving baby at his disposal, rewrote the script again to include action scenes and stunts,

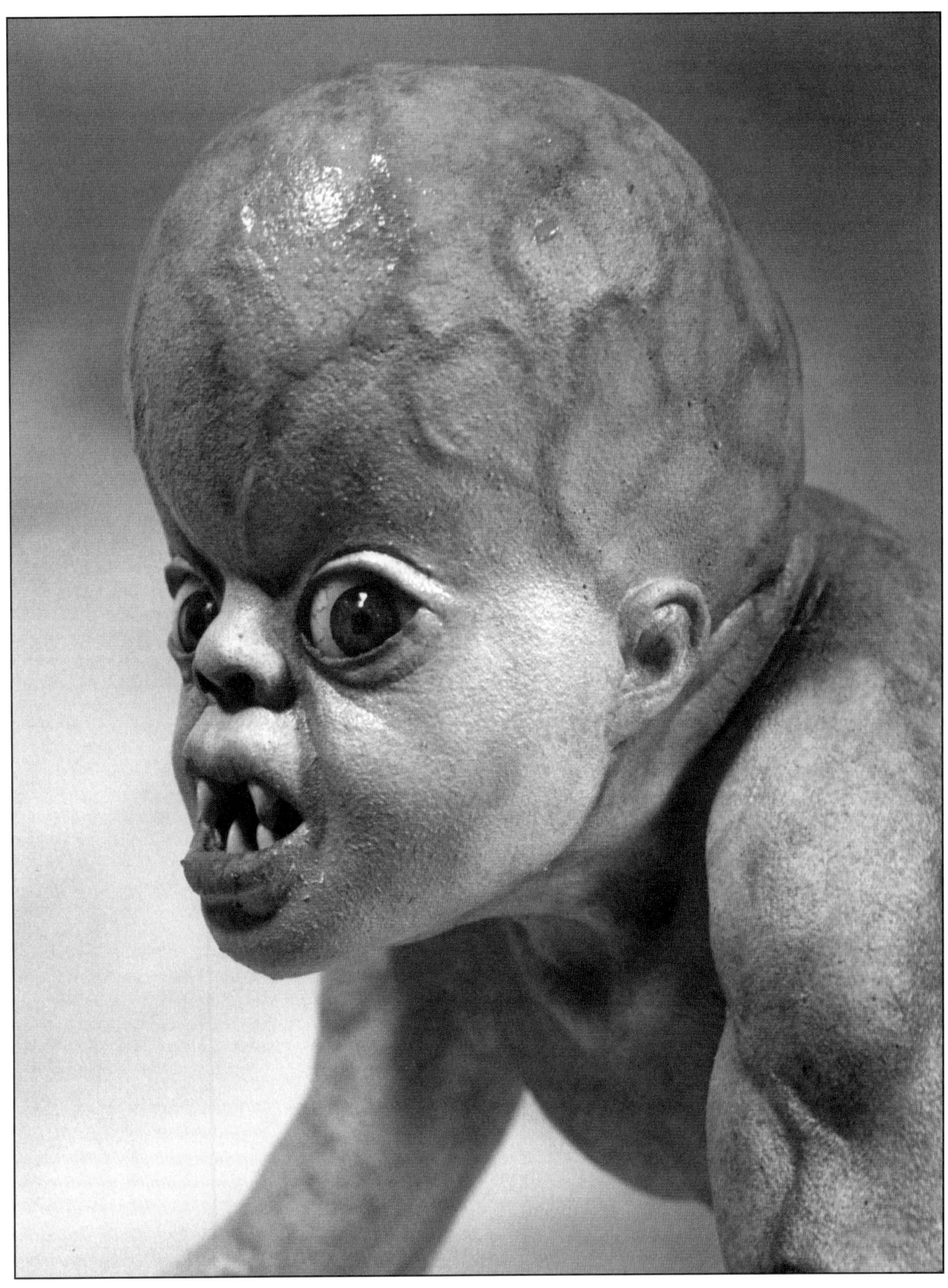

so Baker then had to construct the rest of the baby's body.

Fortunately for Baker, his next project was as far away from babies, monstrous or otherwise, as it was possible to get — turning black actress Cicely Tyson into a 110 year-old former slave for the 1974 television movie *The Autobiography of Miss Jane Pittman*. Recommended for the job by Dick Smith, Baker collaborated on Tyson's old age make-up with Stan Winston, an aspiring actor who got into make-up while waiting for his break and who had previously worked on the award-winning TV movie *Gargoyles* (1972). The pair won an Emmy for their efforts, but while Winston continued with more character-based work (TV's *Roots* [1977]; turning Rod Steiger into W.C. Fields for *W.C. Fields & Me* [1976]), Baker pursued his ambition of creating the ultimate ape suit with John Guillermin's 1976 remake of the classic *King Kong* (1933), starring Jeff Bridges and former model Jessica Lange.

***Below:** Baker sculpting the Octaman.*

When news of Italian movie mogul Dino De Laurentiis' $25,000,000 retelling of *King Kong* was first announced, it was generally assumed that the title ape would be created using stop motion animation as in the 1933 original. The idea was swiftly rejected by *Kong*'s producers, who instead opted for a man-in-an-ape-suit. "When I heard that they were going to remake *King Kong*," recalls Baker, who at the time was working on Jeff Lieberman's man-eating worms shocker *Squirm* (1976), "I said they're probably going to get some idiot in a gorilla suit, instead of doing it right. When they called me and asked me to make the gorilla suit and be *that* idiot, I said, 'Maybe I can bring *something* to this picture.'"

Despite his misgivings about Lorenzo Semple Jr's script, which adopted a disaster movie approach rather than following the original's beauty and the beast theme, Baker felt *Kong* might be his only opportunity to make the ultimate ape suit: "How many films are they going to make about a gorilla where they're going to spend $25,000,000 on it? This was my chance to make a *real* gorilla suit." Baker's hopes were to be continually thwarted by De Laurentiis' insistence that he collaborate with Italian effects specialist Carlo Rambaldi, who would later create the *Alien* (1979) and *E.T.* (1982). De Laurentiis was sold on the idea of Rambaldi creating a forty foot robotic Kong, which Baker felt to be wholly impractical, knowing instinctively that it would never perform the tasks required of it by the script: "They wanted to put all that money into their big robot. I was still a kid, I was pretty young, and I didn't know Dino De Laurentiis from God. I didn't know who he was. I didn't realise he was this big, powerful guy. I would go up to his office and say, 'You're crazy. You're spending a million bucks and this thing is never going to work. You're going to use the gorilla suit instead. So why can't I have that million bucks?'"

Although the movie inexplicably won a special Oscar for special effects, Baker's fears were to be well-founded, as apart from a few shots of Rambaldi's stilted robotic creation, Kong was portrayed almost entirely by Baker wearing his suit. However, even that fell short of Baker's own expectations, as throughout its construction his ideas continually conflicted with those of Rambaldi. And apart from Kong's facial movement, the success of which he concedes was largely due to Rambaldi's greater knowledge of mechanics, Baker feels the suit was an embarrassment: "*King Kong* wasn't that good an experience, but it was fun. It *is* fun to stomp around in miniature cities and throw trains and watch them blow up. It was disappointing, since I could have made the suit a lot better than I was allowed to, and I felt that my opportunity to make a real gorilla suit was lost."

Assisting Baker during *Kong*'s early stages was a sixteen year-old by the name of Rob Bottin, who had been introduced to Baker's work through the pages of *Famous Monsters* in much the same way as Baker had been turned on to the work of Dick Smith. When Bottin was seven he had seen Boris Karloff as the Frankenstein Monster in James Whale's movie and asked his parents where the film-makers had managed to find an actor with a square head. Told it was a special effect, Bottin became intrigued, particularly when he later saw Karloff in another film *sans* make-up. After discovering Karloff had worn a prosthetic make-up for his role in *Frankenstein* (1931), Bottin decided he wanted to be a monster maker and years later, while at high school, he was fortuitously introduced to a girl who knew his idol Rick Baker. Bottin spent a week working on a portrait of the great silent film make-up artist Lon Chaney Sr, which he had framed and gave to the girl on the understanding that the next time she visited Baker she was to hand it to him in return for his autograph. "She came back and told me she couldn't get it," he remembers. Instead, she presented the fourteen year-old Bottin with a photo-montage of Baker's work together with his home phone number. "He wanted to meet me because he didn't believe I was fourteen and could draw that well. I went to Hollywood, met Rick and for some strange reason we just hit it off immediately."

Top and above:
Baker in his Kong head and suit.

"Rob was this big, goofy kid," Baker recollects fondly. "I called him the Baby Hughie after this big duck character that wore diapers and was real big and stoopid. And *that* was Rob." Baker's time with Smith had left an indelible impression on him. "I wanted to be Dick Smith, so I said, 'Come in kid, let me teach you everything I know.' This is what I thought you did: a kid comes over, wants to learn make-up, you teach him everything you know."

"Rick said I could come back to spend more time with him," says Bottin. "I thought he was just being nice, but he gave me some tools, a little bit of clay and a lot of advice. A few months later I saw the girl again and she informed me that Rick was really mad at me because I hadn't had the guts to call him back. I called him up right away and he asked if I wanted to work for him. I started going over to his house all the time. Pretty soon I just started living there. He was kind of a big brother *and* father to me. He told me to lose weight, get a haircut and be respectable. He raised me."

Baker, who was in his mid-twenties at the time and had only recently married, found the situation strange: "All of a sudden I had a fourteen year-old son, and I had to be a dad to this guy. But I liked Rob, and he was fun. He was talented, clever and the years I spent with him were real good times. Rob's my buddy, a friend who had the same kind of love for this kind of stuff and who could appreciate with the eye of an artist good work from bad." ■

Chapter Three

A long time ago, in a galaxy far, far away

Rick Baker, Rob Bottin and Star Wars

Baker's next two projects ran the cinematic gamut from cheesy Z-grade schlock to a block-busting space opera in the guises of William Sachs' excruciatingly moronic *The Incredible Melting Man* (1978) and George Lucas' exuberant, record-breaking *Star Wars* (1977). Although veteran English make-up artist Stuart Freeborn (*Dr. Strangelove: Or How I Learned to Stop Worrying and Love the Bomb* [1963], *2001: A Space Odyssey* [1968]) had already created a number of monsters for the latter's famed Cantina sequence, which was originally filmed at London's Elstree Studios, once back in California Lucas felt the scene needed embellishing with more aliens. Lucas asked effects cameraman Dennis Muren if he could recommend anybody who made rubber monsters, and was put in touch with Baker, who Muren had worked with years before. Baker was already committed to *The Incredible Melting Man*, but met Lucas to view the scene as it existed: "I was really jazzed by the whole concept, I thought what a great idea — a bar full of aliens, what a *cool* thing. What was disappointing, however, was that Lucas didn't want to do as much as I did. He just wanted some masks to add to the scene." Putting together a small crew, which included Bottin, Baker had just six weeks to manufacture twenty background creatures to be integrated into the

Opposite: *One of Bottin's over-sexed fish men from* Humanoids from the Deep.
Left: *Bottin wears Baker's test make-up for* The Incredible Melting Man.

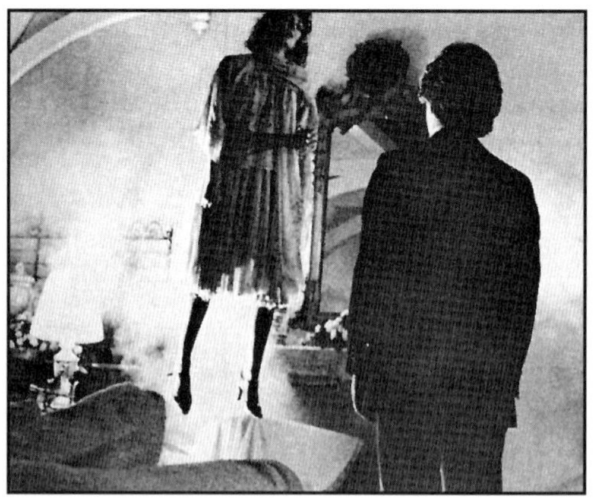

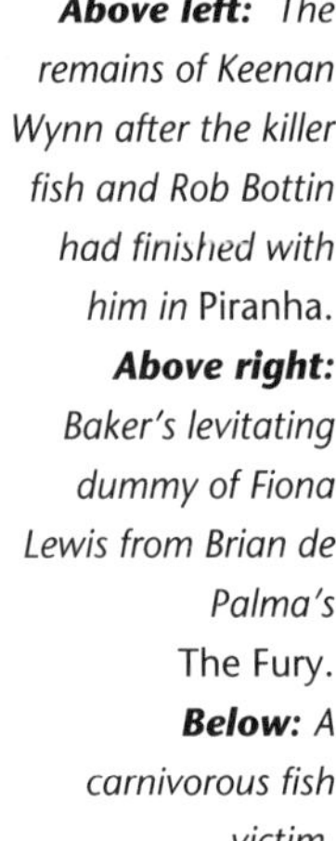

Above left: *The remains of Keenan Wynn after the killer fish and Rob Bottin had finished with him in* Piranha. ***Above right:*** *Baker's levitating dummy of Fiona Lewis from Brian de Palma's* The Fury. ***Below:*** *A carnivorous fish victim.*

scene as shot. Filming took just one day, and while Bottin was on set, Baker, due to his involvement with Sachs' movie, was not. "The stuff in *Star Wars* was definitely not state of the art," comments Baker, "just slip-rubber Halloween-style masks, done very quickly for very little money. And a lot of it was stuff I already had. We did that weird hammerhead thing, but I wanted to do more. I said to George, 'Let's have a little puppet guy that sits on a table, and a space pirate with a weird alien parrot on his shoulder.' I cringe when I see it now because at the time we were capable of doing better stuff. But it's still a neat scene."

For the almost unwatchable *Melting Man*, Baker sculpted four stages of make-up showing the marvellously gooey degeneration of astronaut Alex Rebar who returns to earth suffering from an irreversible space disease. "*The Incredible Melting Man* was a piece of shit," Baker reflects, "but they were actually paying me more money than *Star Wars* and I was doing the actual hands-on make-up."

Next came *The Fury* (1978), Brian De Palma's tale of telekinetic teenagers starring Amy Irving and Kirk Douglas. Under the supervision of Dick Smith, Baker provided a dummy of Fiona Lewis that levitates and spins out of control, as well as one of John Cassavetes that explodes during the film's finale. Significantly, *The Fury* marked the end of Bottin's apprenticeship, and although Baker and Bottin would collaborate on a number of subsequent projects, it was the last time they worked together directly until *The Howling* three years later. "Rick said he thought it was time for me to go out on my own," recalls Bottin, who was eighteen at the time. So while Baker moved on to construct three mutant babies for Larry Cohen's 1978 *It's Alive!* sequel, *It Lives Again*, Bottin began a three-picture stint with Roger

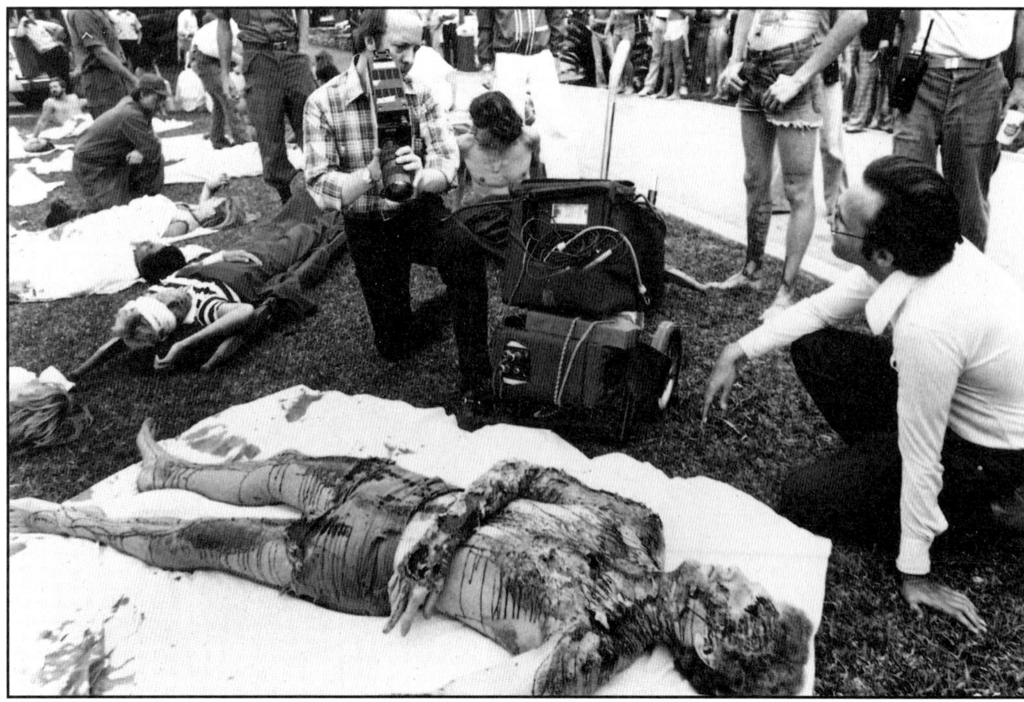

Corman's New World Pictures, linking up with trailer-editor-turned-director Joe Dante for his witty *Jaws* rip-off, *Piranha* (1978). It marked the beginning of a five-film collaboration between director and make-up artist that would continue with *Twilight Zone: The Movie* (1983), *Explorers* (1985), *InnerSpace* (1987) and the film that would make Bottin's name, *The Howling*.

For *Piranha*, Bottin provided the blood-splattered corpses, and can be seen briefly in the finished film as a victim of his voracious fish. For his second New World assignment, Alan Arkush's musical comedy *Rock 'n' Roll High School* (1979), he fabricated a giant mouse suit virtually overnight, as well as playing the rodent himself. But as far as Bottin is concerned, the nadir of his Corman career was Barbara Peeters' trashy *Humanoids from the Deep* (1980), for which he designed the libidinous title creatures and again found himself playing one of them. "It must be one of the worst American films since the fifties," remembers Bottin. "I had to put on a rubber fish suit and rape girls on a beach."

Bottin's next project was Alfred Sole's *Tanya's Island* (1980), starring the still-to-be-discovered Prince protégé Vanity — then known as D.D. Winters — as the imperilled heroine courted by a lusty ape on a desert island. Originally Rick Baker was contracted to provide the ape suit, but after sculpting a maquette of the creature he left to both build and play Sidney the gorilla who befriends the fast-diminishing Lily Tomlin in Joel Schumacher's *The Incredible Shrinking Woman* (1981). Baker therefore recommended Bottin be brought in to finish off his design for the half baboon/half orangutan creature. Little seen, the film would be one of the last times that Bottin toiled away in relative obscurity, for both his career and his craft were about to take off in spectacular fashion. ■

Above: *Heather Menzies tends to Bradford Dillman's Bottin-manufactured wounds in the closing moments of* Piranha.
Left: *D.D. Winters enjoys a clinch with the ape from* Tanya's Island, *designed by Baker, built by Bottin.*

Chapter Four

State of flux: rubber rules the screen

Transformations in Altered States and The Howling

The early eighties saw special make-up effects take on a life and celebrity of their own, thanks largely to a succession of showy transformation movies that began with *Altered States*, *The Howling* and *An American Werewolf in London* (1981), and which were taken to surreal extremes by Rob Bottin's visceral shape-shifting extra-terrestrial in John Carpenter's *The Thing* (1982). Again it was Smith who paved the way for the effects explosion with his work on Ken Russell's cosmic mind-blower *Altered States*, in which Harvard scientist William Hurt's experiments with sensory deprivation and hallucinogenic drugs cause him to physically regress. Smith created three full-body foam-latex suits showing Hurt in a dramatic state of flux, as well as two for Blair Brown, the first revealing her *sans* skin, with her muscles and veins exposed, with the second, nicknamed Burnt Brown, looking somewhat like molten lava. Smith also made Hurt's forehead bulge and skin ripple with a system of wafer-thin bladders hooked up to air tubes covered with realistic skin appliances.

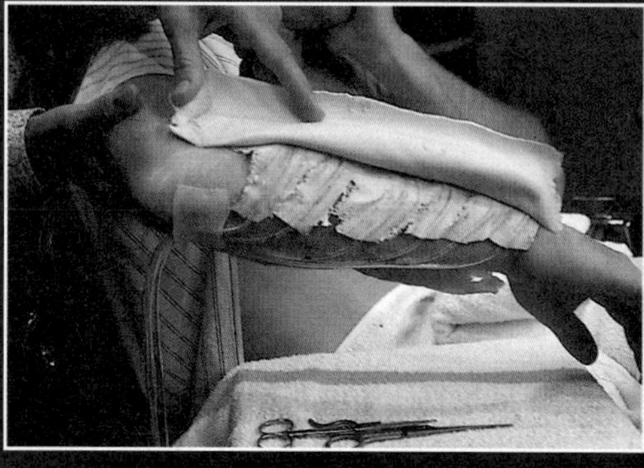

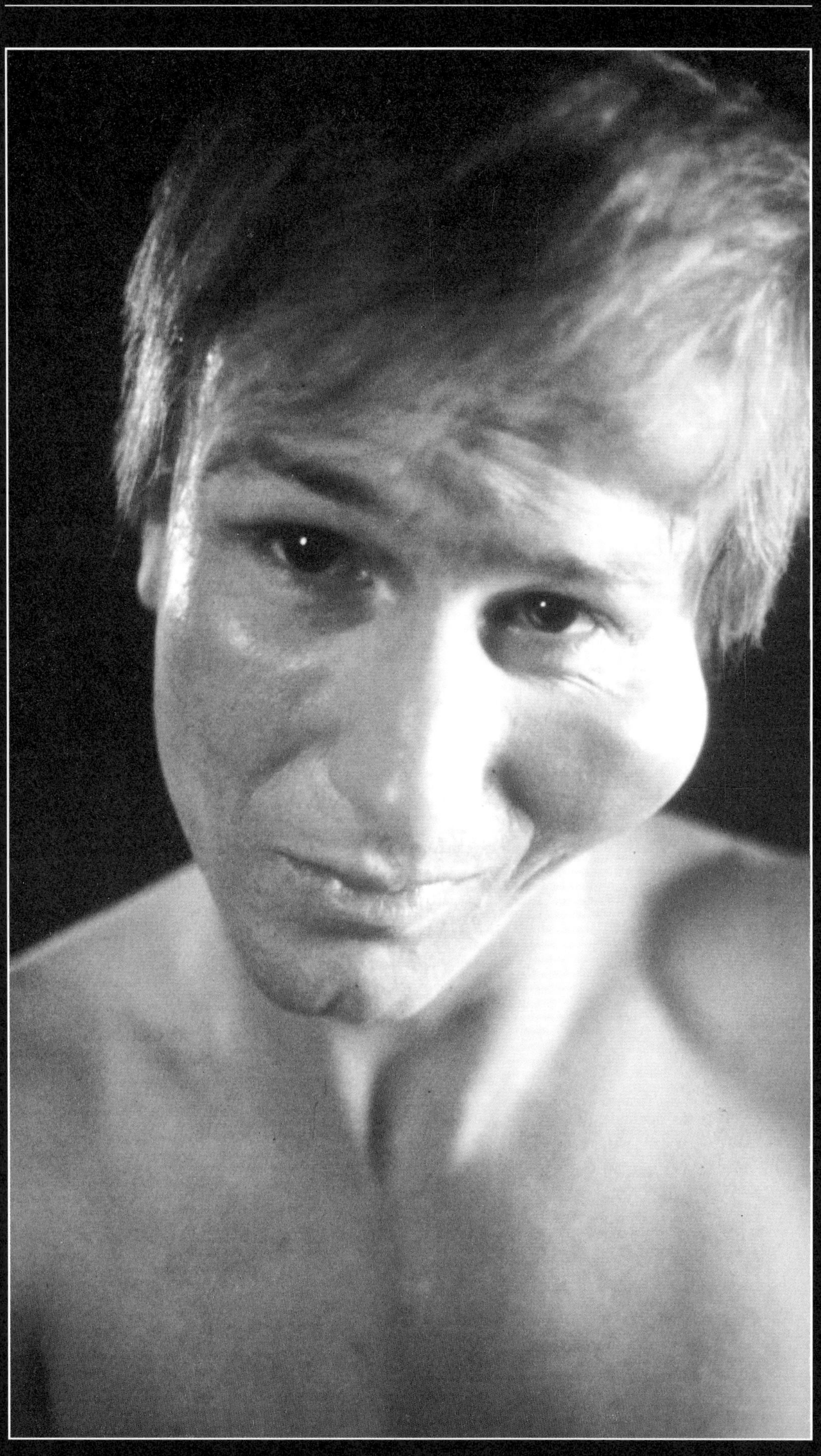

Opposite top: *Blair Brown in one of Dick Smith's rubber suits from* Altered States. ***Opposite bottom left:*** *A series of wafer-thin bladders are applied to William Hurt's arm for the start of his* Altered States *transformation.* ***Opposite bottom right:*** *Once the bladders are in place, a thin foam latex appliance is glued over the top, and when inflated sequentially a disturbing rippling effect is achieved.* ***Left:*** *William Hurt with facial bladder from* Altered States.

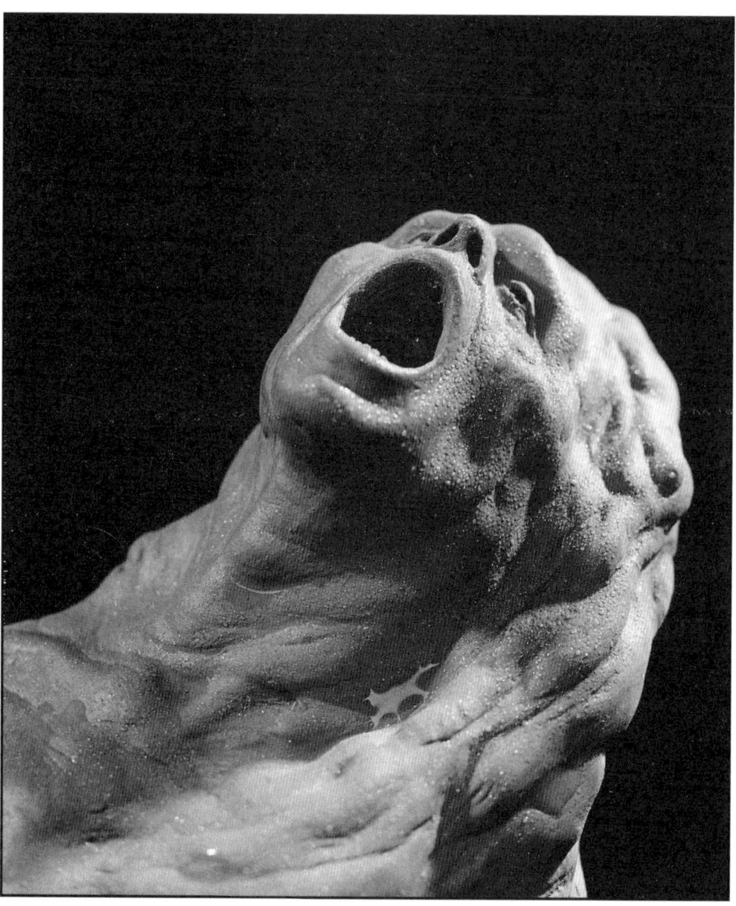

It was Rick Baker, however, who, following Smith's lead, took make-up effects into new areas of innovation with his aptly-named 'change-o-heads' (elaborate fake heads covered with flexible skins which were stretched using rods, cables or air bladders). They formed the basis of virtually every transformation from *The Howling* and *An American Werewolf in London* up until the advent of computer morphing.

Baker had been toying with the idea of a 'change-o-head' ever since *Schlock*, when John Landis told him about a script he had written, a couple of years earlier, when he was eighteen and working as a gofer on *Kelly's Heroes* (1970) in Yugoslavia. Landis' script was titled *An American Werewolf in London* and called for a dramatic transformation sequence from man into werewolf, which he insisted should go far beyond anything ever seen before, graphically twisting the human form into lupine shape on screen and in real time, and without relying on the standard techniques.

"The original idea for the 'change-o-head' came from the fact I thought about having hair grow on the person's face without doing lap dissolves," says Baker. "I figured you could do it in reverse by pulling hair *in*. Since you couldn't do that on a real person's head, I thought, 'What if we made a likeness of this person, punched the hair in it and then pulled it back through.' So I thought, if we could do that, why couldn't we push the shapes around a little bit too?"

Above and right: *Two of the three maquettes Smith made to conceptualise Hurt's transformation in Ken Russell's* Altered States.

Having gone to school with Mark Whitney, whose father, John, was one of the pioneers of computer animation in the sixties, Landis had a clear idea of how such a transformation could be achieved. His intention was to take a series of make-ups that would represent successive stages of the werewolf transformation and then computer generate the in-betweens: "I went to John Whitney back in 1969 and asked him if this was possible. He said, 'Absolutely, but we don't know if we have the hardware for it.'"

What Landis had in mind would later be commonly known as morphing. However, at that time mainframe computers weren't powerful enough to create such an effect, and it would be almost two decades before morphing would make its début in a feature film with *Willow* (1988). "We had heard about morphing back then," confirms Baker, "but the technology wasn't quite there. And what Whitney showed us was stuff any kid who's got a 3D program on his Apple Mac can do now — *for a hundred bucks*. It looked cool, but it didn't look *real*, and it *needs* to look real."

Left: *Rick Baker sculpting the split-faced freak in Tobe Hooper's* The Funhouse.

Baker promised to provide the effects for Landis' film whenever the project came to fruition. But as the years went by, and Landis moved on to direct *The Kentucky Fried Movie* (1977) — featuring a Rick Baker ape (nicknamed Dino after *Kong* producer Dino De Laurentiis) — *National Lampoon's Animal House* (1978) and *The Blues Brothers* (1980), his *American Werewolf* script, with its unconventional mix of horror and comedy, showed little sign of making it off the page, despite being optioned on several occasions. So when Baker was approached by director Joe Dante to provide the werewolves for *The Howling*, he decided that if he couldn't use the 'change-o-heads' he had designed for Landis' feature, he might as well get some mileage out of them here. Baker, however, was still reluctant to give his full commitment to the project, since he wished to remain in a position to take on *American Werewolf* should the film ever get made. "I suggested they went to Rob," recalls Baker. Bottin went along as insurance should Baker have to relinquish his direct involvement due to his commitment to Landis.

Working together for the first time since *The Fury*, Baker and Bottin decided to do a test reel of the transformation scene in the hope of getting a bigger effects budget: "We kicked around a lot of ideas and at that point I started thinking I was kind of cutting my own throat, telling Rob all this stuff I had intended to use for *Werewolf*. But I ended up telling Rob most of what I planned to do anyway, because if *Werewolf* never got made, at least I'd have been involved in a film that had the sort of transformation scene I'd always wanted to do." But as Baker was sculpting the last stage of one of the werewolf heads for the test, he realised that what he was doing was just *too* similar to what he had in mind for Landis' film, and handed over the reins to his twenty-one year-old protégé, though he remained on board as a technical consultant. Fortunately, *American Werewolf* was finally given the go-ahead while he was completing the test footage on *The Howling*.

"It was a very tricky position for Rick because this technology was only developing at the time," recalls *The Howling*'s director Joe Dante, "and for him to apportion which ideas he was going to use on his own picture and which ones to help Rob with must have been very difficult. I don't know how much consulting Rob did with Rick, but I do know that I saw a test Rick shot on video of a snout growing on somebody which was really scary."

ALTERED STATES BODY SUITS

The three full-body suits that Smith created for *Altered States* were, Smith considers, some of his best work. In the film, Dr Edward Jessup, a psychophysiologist, manages to change his physical make-up as a result of his experiments.

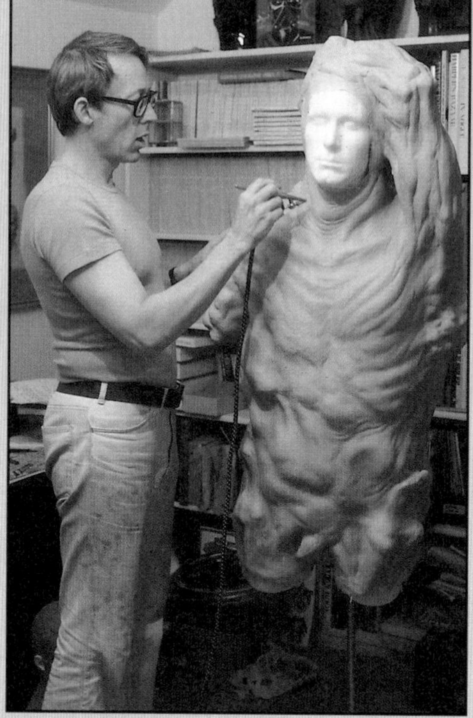

The suits proved problematic from the very first production meetings. Smith had to realise an extremely abstract concept in three dimensions and create a man whose "molecular glue", as Smith called it, was coming apart.

A sculptor was hired to pin down a design for Jessup's deterioration, but while Smith thought the sculptures good, they overlooked the suits ultimate need to be applied to a human body. Therefore, Smith decided to produce his own. The three maquettes (or scale models) showed Jessup's body in progressive states of fusion. Smith's work paid off, as the dramatically lit photographs of his models helped get the film back off the ground during one of the troubled production's delays.

To make the actual suits, Smith needed a cast of actor William Hurt, in various contorted positions. For the first suit, a cast from the chest up was needed, with his right hand reaching over his head and grabbing his left cheek, a position impossible for Hurt to hold for the requisite fifteen minutes it takes to apply the casting material.

Smith's solution was to first apply a bald cap, vaseline Hurt's body completely and place a large pipe in his mouth for breathing. Then, with a team of three, he used large squares of sacking material, dipped into a fast setting plaster, and threw them on to the actor's body. Luckily for Hurt, Smith managed to remove the mould in less than five minutes, before the heat generated by the setting plaster became painful. The mould was filled with plaster and a cast produced, onto which Smith sculpted the rippling body distortions. After being moulded and cast in foam latex, the suit was carefully donned and the head piece glued down around Hurt's face. Putting on the suits was no easy matter, as one of them required the actor to keep his arms behind his back, causing a considerable lack of blood circulation.

Ironically, all three of Jessup's suits were obliterated by optical effects added in post production, covering up some of Smith's greatest work. ■

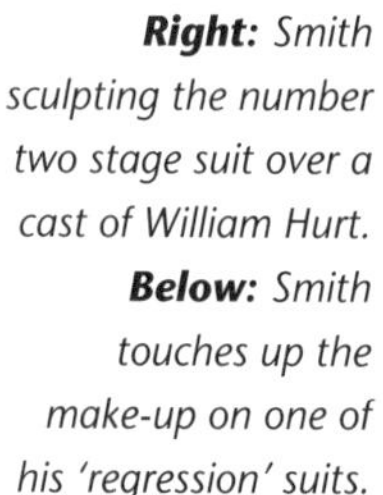

Right: *Smith sculpting the number two stage suit over a cast of William Hurt.* ***Below:*** *Smith touches up the make-up on one of his 'regression' suits.*

Left: *Belinda Belaski on the receiving end of Bottin's werewolf.* ***Below:*** *A puppet head of actor Robert Picardo as Eddie Quist in* The Howling. *Later, realistic heads like this would become a Bottin speciality.*

Adapted by John Sayles from Gary Brander's novel of the same name, *The Howling* necessitated Bottin creating a number of werewolf transformations as well as a ten foot tall werewolf, though the film's highlight was always to be the show-stopping metamorphosis of long-haired lycanthropic murderer Eddie Quist. "The original idea was to try to do it all in one shot, which now can be done with morphing," explains Dante, "and, frankly, now that I've seen morphing, I'm glad that we didn't do it that way. We wanted to get away from the Lon Chaney Jr werewolves because it had been done so many times that it didn't seem like there was much point. And since part of the concept of *The Howling* was to bring the werewolf into the 1980s, we wanted to try to do effects and transformations people hadn't seen before."

"They wanted the most incredible transformation ever filmed, and they kept asking me, 'Are you sure you can really do all this stuff?'" recalls Bottin who, due to the sheer enormity of the task, had to assemble a crew of more than a dozen technicians. Fittingly, they included another three of Baker's protégés: Steve Johnson, whom Bottin had previously worked with on *Tanya's Island* and John Carpenter's *The Fog* (1980); Greg Cannom, who would later win Oscars for *Bram Stoker's Dracula* (1992) and *Mrs Doubtfire* (1993); and Shawn McEnroe who, along with Johnson, would join Baker on *American Werewolf.*

"We had been talking about using miniatures, replacement animation, just about anything you can think of to make the change come about," recalls Bottin. "Rick said he was going to use air bladders and other techniques to make a mask change, and I put together what I'd picked up from Rick, along with some techniques I'd used before."

Bottin's solution for Quist's transformation employed both Baker's 'change-o-heads' and Smith's *Altered States* bladder technique, and was achieved using a combination of an actor (Robert Picardo), wearing pulsating bladders on his face, covered by foam appliances, and several 'change-o-heads'. These were modelled on a series of life casts of Picardo, who was instructed by Bottin to pull "werewolf faces" while his head was being cast. Bottin's idea was that if he sculpted onto an already extreme expression, then the mask would already have life in it. Fitted out with an assortment of levers, rods, cables and bladders, the 'change-o-heads' were capable of a wide range of movements.

Wearing Bottin's elaborate prosthetics was stage actor Picardo in his cinematic début: "*The Howling* was primarily a dozen condoms glued onto my face — before they were as fashionable as they are now. It was an effect the audience had never seen before, because at one moment the actor's face was as we had seen it throughout the

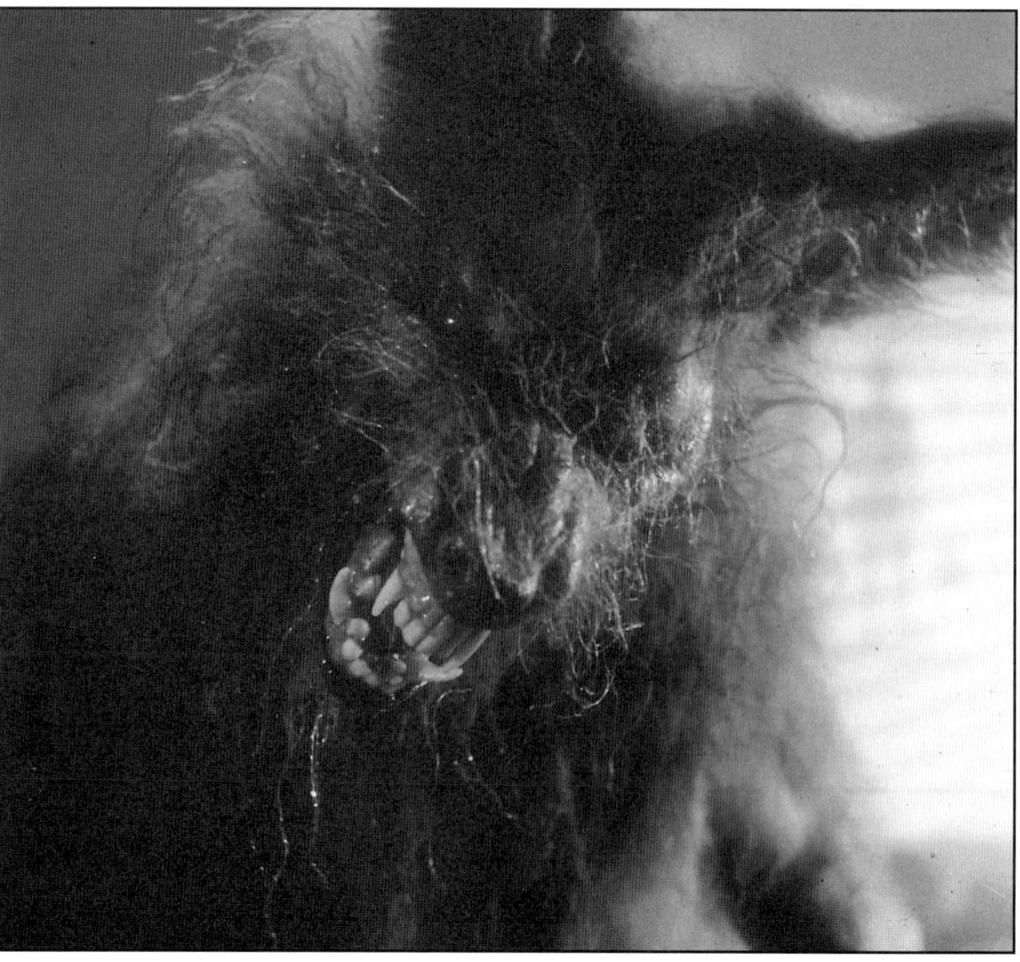

***Above:** A close-up of one of* The Howling*'s 'change-o-heads'.* ***Right:** Bottin's* Howling *werewolf in its final stage.*

whole movie, and then, all of a sudden, it was bubbling like a pot of chilli. Because it was a new technique, you never quite knew until the day of shooting where the problems were going to arise. The most unsettling part was this enormous bladder on my neck. When they inflated it, it completely closed your throat. I couldn't breathe at all. So if you happened to be breathing in for your next snarl when they inflated the bladder, it was as if Arnold Schwarzenegger had grabbed you by the throat." Picardo would later don more rubber for both Bottin and Dante in *Explorers* and *InnerSpace*, as well as for Ridley Scott's *Legend* (1985).

Though the transition from man to werewolf was always intended to be a smooth one, circumstances conspired to make it more erratic. "Rick's original test had all been done very smoothly and subtly, more like morphing actually," recalls Dante. "But when we came to do it on the set, sometimes things would pop out. We tended to view that as a mistake, so when we were cutting the scenes we would try to cut around the parts that changed abruptly. But then the sound effects guy came in and he gave us some bone cracks. We started putting them on the pops, and all of a sudden they looked like they were on purpose. So the whole concept of the transformation changed. Instead of being a sort of supernatural, smooth, gliding change, it became this tortuous, painful, bone-cracking metamorphosis. In addition to covering up our mistakes, it actually improved the whole scene."

One thing Bottin especially wanted to avoid was a werewolf design that resembled anything seen before. "All the transitional heads, masks and make-ups don't really resemble a werewolf so much as a demonic person who keeps changing," said Bottin, who went through more than a dozen different designs before settling upon a concept for the werewolf's final look.

Steve Johnson recalls the design process with awe: "When Rob sculpted the head for the wolf puppet, he sat down and sculpted one that looked great. I loved it, I thought it was wonderful. But he ripped it to shreds, threw it out the window, and did another one. It was *ten times better*. I had never seen a werewolf so cool. But he ripped it up, threw it out the window, did another one. And it was even *better*. I was losing my mind, I was salivating. But he ripped it up, threw it out the window and did another one. And it was like five or six heads into it before he settled for something — and it was *brilliant*."

"When you're doing effects, you're just trying to get them to be okay and not to look like effects," explains Dante. "When you're there, and you know how it's done, and you see how phoney it looks, you do everything you can to keep it from looking as phoney as you know it really is. You move the camera, you do it with lights, you do *anything*. So there is never really much of a sense of 'Boy. What geniuses we are, we are really doing great stuff.' We didn't realise how much of a splash the effects in *The Howling* were going to make until the studio saw them, and started to send word out to the exhibitors that this picture was gonna be *really* cool." ■

Top: *Director Joe Dante looks on as Rob Bottin demonstrates one of his 'change-o-heads' from* The Howling. ***Above:*** *Bottin rests between takes wearing* The Howling *werewolf's puppet attack head on his arm.*

Chapter Five

There's a bad moon rising

Baker and An American Werewolf in London

Despite its witty script, solid acting, knowing direction and atmospheric cinematography, it was inevitably Rob Bottin's incredible transformation effects that stole all the headlines upon *The Howling*'s US release. This situation placed a severe strain on Baker and Bottin's relationship, as well as putting Baker in the unenviable position of having to top his former student. "When *The Howling* came out first, I said, 'Boy, that was a *big* mistake,'" recalls Baker of his decision to share information with Bottin. "And the press made a big deal about this young kid who did these neat things that nobody had seen before. Rob took my ideas and added his own, which made my job on *Werewolf* that much more difficult. In retrospect, I feel sharing as much information as I did was a mistake, and it did take some of the impact out of my transformation. John Landis was pissed off by

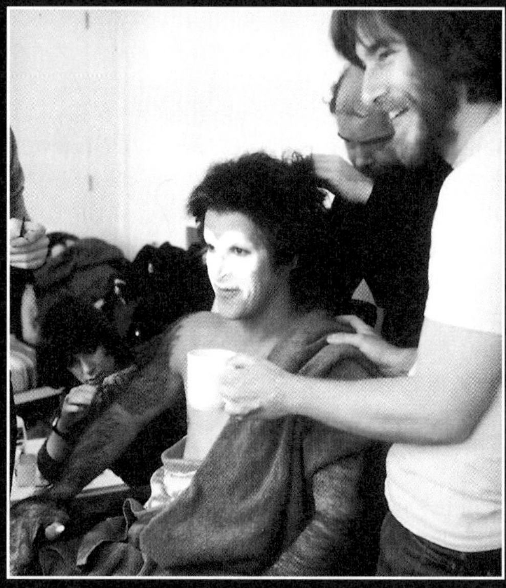

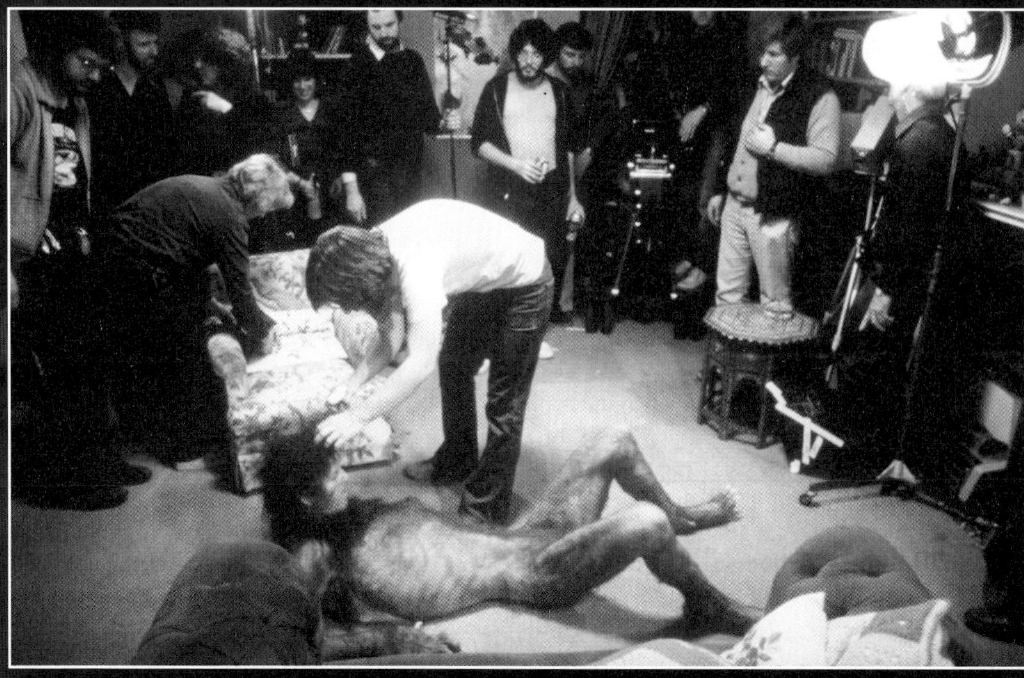

Opposite top: *David Naughton undergoes the first stages of Rick Baker's werewolf transformation in* An American Werewolf in London.
Opposite bottom: *Rick Baker adjusts David Naughton's hair in preparation for a take.*
Left: *One of the early stage change-o-heads.*

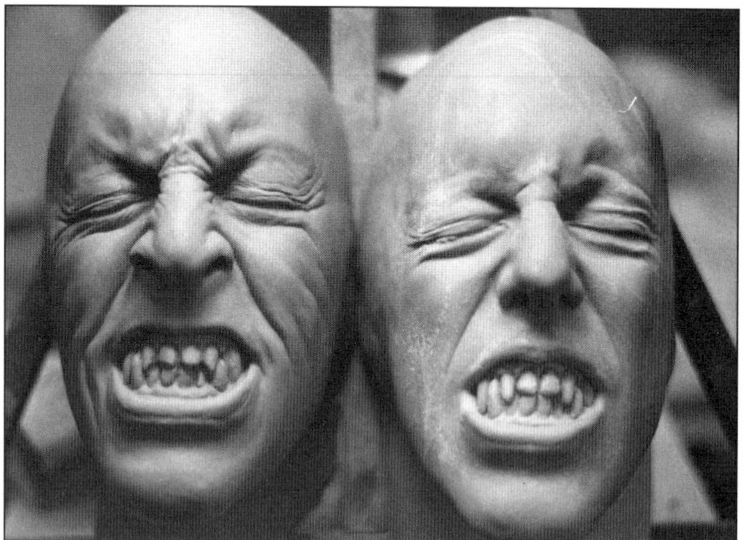

Above left: *A lifecast of Naughton with false teeth, next to the sculpted first change-o-head.* ***Above right:*** *Baker crewmember Tom Hester fitting claws to a pair of transformation hands for* An American Werewolf. ***Right:*** *Baker and Kevin Brennan prepare to shoot the stretching change-o-hand, while director John Landis looks on.*

it and so was I."

"It was very aggravating at the time," reflects Landis. "But what Joe (*Dante*) did was the opposite of what I had in mind. In *The Howling* there are all these cutaways, and the transformation takes place in the dark. In the dark you can get away with a lot. For *American Werewolf*, it was always my intention that the transformation be very painful, for it to be on camera, in bright light, with no cutaways. I said to Rick, 'I don't want any cutaways.' In the whole sequence there's just one: to Mickey Mouse. It's all there, it's all *happening*. Those are pretty outrageous demands on the make-ups. What we did was so revolutionary at the time, but since then it's been done to death — all that *stretching*. I remember when I saw *Company of Wolves* (1984), I went 'all right. We've seen it already.'"

Since Baker felt the bladder effect that had formed the basis of the transformations in both *Altered States* and *The Howling* would be considered passé by the time *American Werewolf* finally made it into theatres, he was determined to try a different approach for his, one that would go way beyond the 'change-o-heads' he had intended for *The Howling* and more into full 'change-o-*body*' territory. Since the script called for every part of actor David Naughton's anatomy to undergo an on-screen metamorphosis, his intention was to build a full-size 'change-o' figure. But Landis specifically wanted the effect to come together bit by bit, to enhance the dramatic effect, so instead Baker constructed a series of 'change-o' sections, including head, hands, legs and back.

As the full moon rises outside nurse Jenny Agutter's London flat, werewolf-in-waiting David Kessler (Naughton) begins to sweat profusely, rip-

RICK BAKER THE APE MAN

Ever since he was thirteen, Rick Baker had been consumed by the desire to make the ultimate ape suit, one indistinguishable from the real thing. It was a dream that he eventually realised with his remarkable simian creations for Michael Apted's *Gorillas in the Mist* in 1988. Baker made his first sculptured gorilla head at nineteen and created the ape-man make-up for John Landis' horror spoof *Schlock*, but his first serious attempt at a realistic ape suit had been *King Kong*. "The more I read about apes and looked at them, the more fascinated I became," he admits. "Also, I had the misconception that most people have that they're monsters. But, in fact, they're quite noble, gentle animals."

For *The Incredible Shrinking Woman*, Joel Schumacher's updating of Jack Arnold's fifties classic *The Incredible Shrinking Man* (1957), Baker created and played the ape Sidney that befriends Lily Tomlin's title character while both are held captive by unscrupulous scientists. Baker delivers an impressive performance as the intelligent gorilla with a sense of humour. His close study of his subject matter is clearly evident in Sidney's expressive mannerisms: "I've studied expressions and performance, so when I wear a mask or put a make-up on and move it around, trying to make an expression, I've kind of learnt what to do. I've spent my life in front of a mirror making faces."

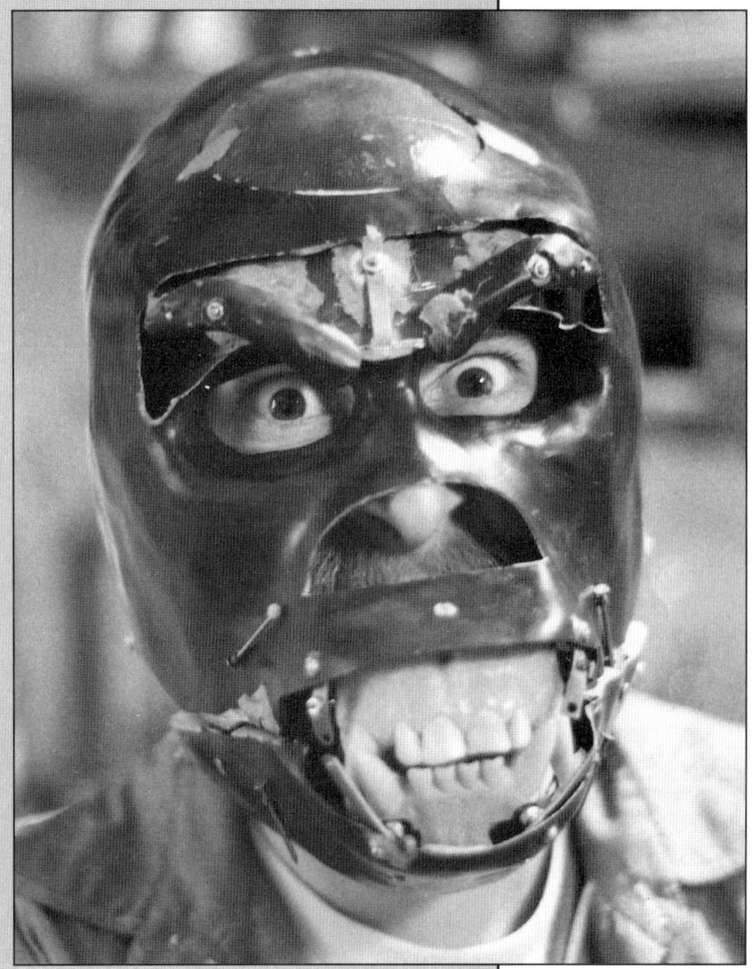

For *Greystoke: The Legend of Tarzan Lord of the Apes,* Hugh Hudson's stately adaptation of Edgar Rice Burroughs' adventure yarn, Baker assembled a crew of around forty artists and technicians to realise Tarzan's ape family. While not wholly accurate in biological terms, being a mixture of chimpanzee and gorilla, at the time Baker's apes were easily the most convincing committed to film.

"*Greystoke* is the hardest I've ever worked on any film. I sculpted almost every one of the heads, painted them and put the hair on them, and did the mechanics, as well as having a large crew I had to baby-sit. It was like day-and-night work; I really aged on that film. Figs *(pictured left)* is my favourite ape because he's the most bizarre and extreme character. He was based on a real chimp called Flo who was this sort of ugly mutant chimp with a weird nose. I did the sculpture real fast and I think I managed to capture a really neat character." ■

Above: *Baker stares out from the underskull on to which the mechanics are installed for Sidney the gorilla from* The Incredible Shrinking Woman. ***Left:*** *The ape Figs from* Greystoke *— a Baker favourite.* ***Far left:*** *David Naughton wearing hand appliances and laid on hair at the start of his transformation in* An American Werewolf in London.

***Right:** A change-o-head with a growling snout from* An American Werewolf in London.
***Far right:** Baker's concept painting for Jack Goodman.*
***Opposite top left:** Jack's claw wound at the sculpting stage.*
***Opposite top right:** Griffin Dunne wearing the prosthetic appliance.*
***Opposite bottom:** Jack in a greater state of decomposition.*
***Below left:** Only Naughton's head and arms are his own. The rest of his body is a rod puppet controlled from beneath the set.*
***Below right:** A werewolf mask appliance.*

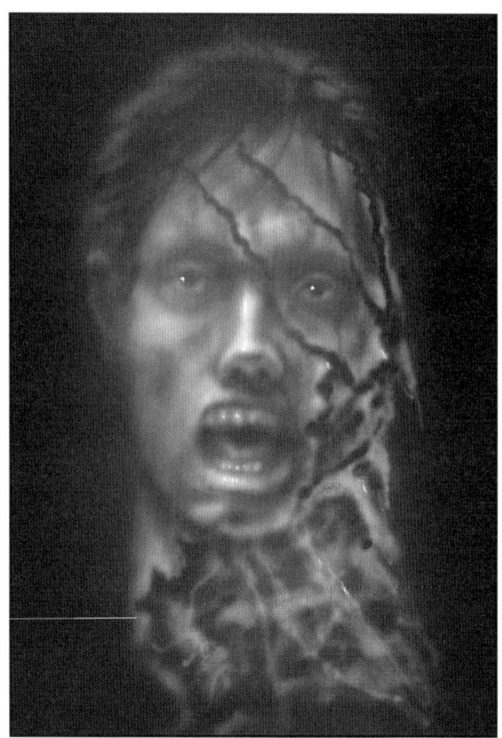

ping off his T-shirt and jeans as the first effects of lycanthropy begin to rage through his body. First, his right hand elongates (an effect achieved by using a 'change-o-hand'), then, as his face and body become more hirsute, Naughton's legs extend, his backbones reform themselves into a new configuration, before two of Baker's 'change-o-heads' are employed to distort the last vestiges of Naughton's human shell as his face takes on lupine form.

Since it was always Landis' intention for the transformation to be as realistic as possible, the scene was scripted to take place in a brightly lit room, a situation that Baker disagreed with from the very beginning: "I argued with John a lot about it. I said, 'This stuff works better when you can control the lighting, because it's fake. It's *good* fake but it's still fake, and it needs all the help it can get. And then he was playing *that* music that goes *totally* against it. I was going, 'You know John, what's neat about film-making is that you can create an atmosphere that leads you to think that something is scarier than it really is. Couldn't you use the music to kinda *enhance* the transformation?' John's answer was that it was important for it to appear real, that this was happening to a

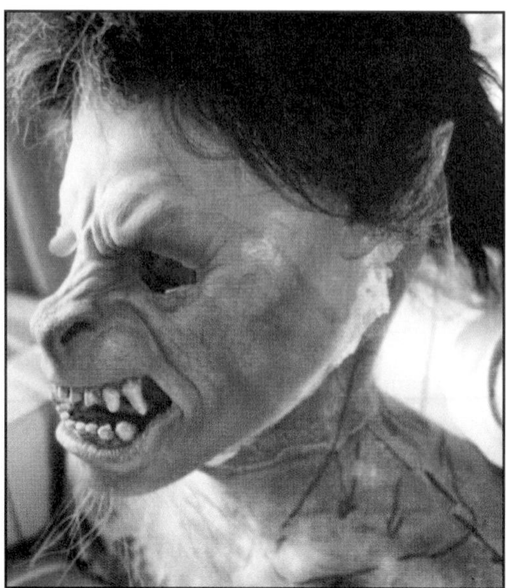

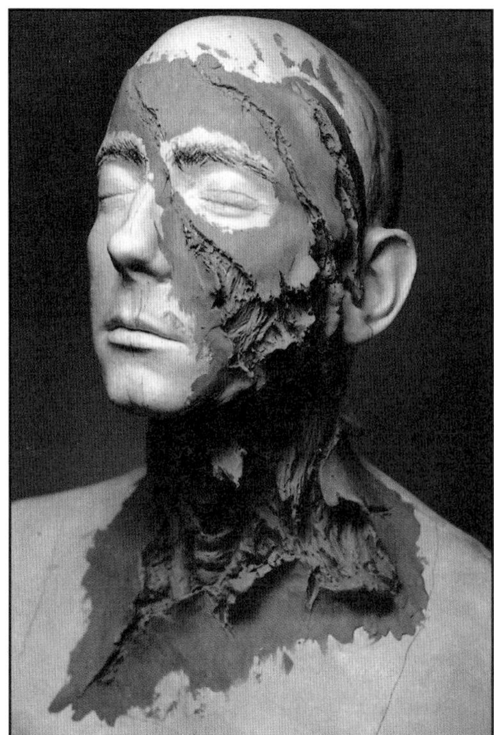

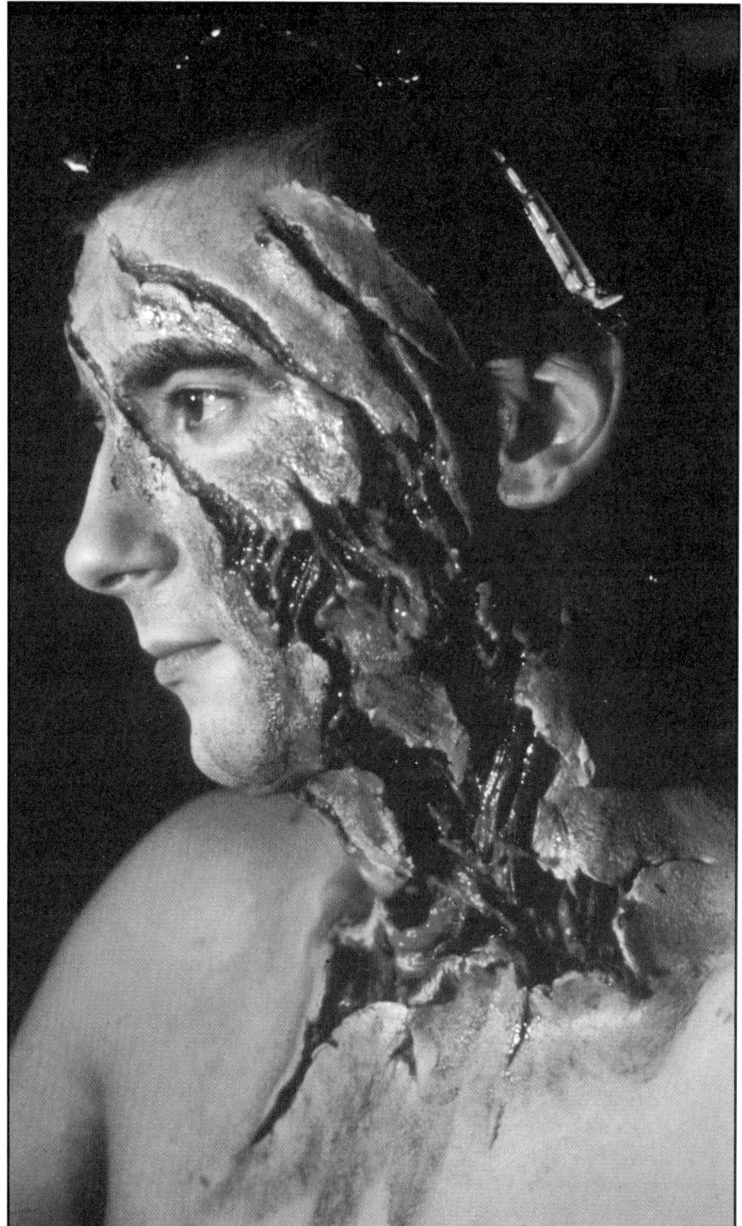

real guy. But I think the same transformation could have looked a lot better with more careful lighting and more shadows here and there."

"Less is more with these things," muses Dante, "because the more you leave to people's imaginations, the better the stuff looks. I think the effects in *The Howling* are much more primitive than those in *American Werewolf,* but I've always felt, and I'm sure that John would disagree with me, that ours are photographed better, because they were darker and there was more left to the imagination. There is so much light on the transformation scene in *American Werewolf* that what are really brilliant effects, don't come off as well as they might. The more you overlight it, the worse it looks, particularly if it's made of latex, rubber, or whatever. I believe lower key is more realistic for this kind of material. And that particular scene, I felt, was overlit."

Ironically, on reflection, Landis agrees: "Looking back on *Werewolf,* what was ridiculous was my intention of showing the metamorphosis in bright light."

In addition to Naughton's transformation, Baker and his seven-man crew also had to create a full-size walking werewolf for the film's finale. "I said I wanted it to be a *big wolf,*" recalls Landis, who wanted a creature that walked on four legs as opposed to the werewolves seen in *The Howling* which walked upright. Only glimpsed during the sequence on the London Underground, though seen more fully during the climactic scenes in

Piccadilly Circus, the wolf was simply a member of Baker's crew, wearing a furred suit and a cable-operated werewolf head, lying on a board with his arms inside the wolf's front legs. The wolf's back legs were puppeteered from behind by rods, and the whole rig was pushed around like a wheelbarrow. "Rick will definitely disagree with me on this, but I think I showed the wolf too much," says Landis. "I was enamoured of it — I loved it. But in fact, the only shot of the wolf I really like is when the guy is being pursued on the Underground and he falls down on the escalator. He looks down and there's that long shot where you see it come out. That's neat, because the wolf is so *big*. Yeah, I like

***Right:** The fully transformed werewolf — a man in a suit lying on a trolley, its back legs puppeteered with rods.* ***Opposite top:** Baker sculpting a werewolf maquette.* ***Opposite middle:** Sculpting one of the Nazi demons.* ***Opposite bottom:** Baker and his crew pose with the various stages of the werewolf and Jack puppet in their temporary London workshop.* ***Below:** The final werewolf head sans fur.*

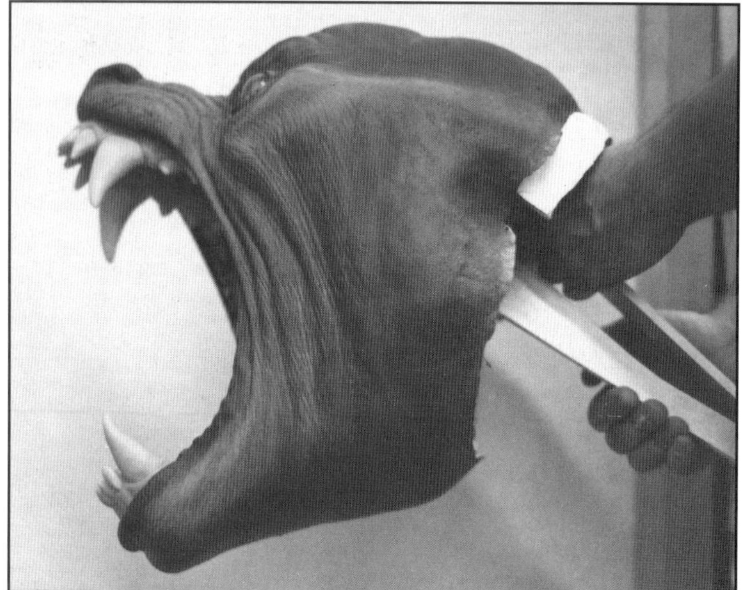

that, but I still think I showed it too much."

Inevitably, Baker disagrees: "I wish the wolf was in it a little bit *more*. There were a couple of shots that were really neat, though John didn't use them. John's attitude was, 'I'm never going to show the wolf.' But I figured, well, he probably will. To this day, John says, 'The wolf's in the movie too much.' I like the wolf. I think it's neat."

While much time and effort was put into creating the title character, Baker also had to provide the make-up for Jack Goodman, David's best friend (played by Griffin Dunne). Goodman is the first victim of the werewolf that infects David at the film's beginning, who returns to haunt his friend throughout the picture as one of the walking dead, each time looking more and more decomposed. Initially, Dunne wore extensive prosthetic appliances covering the left side of his face and throat, and eventually his whole face and hands. But as Dunne's character deteriorates further, Baker felt it necessary to create an animatronic puppet which took up to six people to operate, with Dunne himself controlling the jaw mechanism as well as providing the voice. "All you can do make-up wise to a real person is *add*, and I wanted to *subtract*," explains Baker. "The puppet, based on the real actor's facial structure, allowed us to do that. We went from the actor's face and worked down."

"Griffin got profoundly depressed wearing that stuff," remembers Landis, "it really freaked him out. It's one thing to know that you're going to have your face covered with latex and be made up as a zombie, and *then* to see huge gouges out of your face. It was pretty shocking at the time too. I mean, now gory stuff is so common, but then it was pretty gruesome."

Baker, however, doesn't feel Jack's make-up is gruesome enough: "I don't like the fact that Jack doesn't have blood on him. That's another thing I argued with John about. When Jack comes back the first time he has a big hole in his throat and I wanted the blood to run over to the other side of his face. But John didn't want it. I still don't agree with him on that. I kinda cringe at that. I think that looks funny. Actually, I don't like the second stage of the Jack make-up either, I think the colour's bad."

To this day Baker remains highly critical of his work on *Werewolf*. Due to a lack of pre-production time, he first applied many of the transformation make-ups on the day they were shot. Baker remembers the first day of the week-long transformation shoot all too clearly: "It was the day after the wrap party. Now, I'm not really a party animal guy, but I had a young crew, we drank some beers and the next day I had a really bad hangover for the first time in my life. I felt like shit and I had to do the hardest transformation I had ever done. We got to one stage that was just ridiculous. David Naughton had a big mane of hair, goofy paws and a big chest on, it was stupid-looking. David had these hands on, and could only use his thumbs because his fingers were inside them. I was still feeling a bit sick, and there was David eating fish and chips with his stupid hands and a goon suit on. I have a very vivid memory of this, and I remember thinking, 'Oh God, it's the end of my career.' Fortunately it's not in there real long."

Baker needn't have worried. His work justifiably won him the first competitive Oscar for make-up at the 1982 Academy Awards, beating Stan Winston for *Heartbeeps* (1982) and taking him to the top of his profession. ■

Chapter Six

The grandaddy of all monsters

Rob Bottin and The Thing

With effects technology advancing to such a degree that a man could convincingly be transformed into a wolf, it was inevitable that writers and directors would begin to push the cinematic boundaries of not only what was possible, but what was *conceivable*. A prime example was *The Thing*, John Carpenter's dazzlingly visceral remake of *The Thing from Another World* (1951). When producer Howard Hawks and director Christian Nyby first filmed John W. Campbell Jr's novella *Who Goes There?* as *The Thing from Another World* they eschewed all reference to Campbell's concept of an alien able to mimic and

Opposite top: *Rob Bottin — monster maker.* ***Opposite bottom:*** *A close-up of The Thing from the Norwegian camp. Beautifully detailed, but barely glimpsed in the finished film.* ***Left:*** *Bottin poses with one of his creations from* The Thing.

Right: *An incredibly realistic husky from* The Thing.
Below right: *Monster concepts — the result of brainstorming sessions by Bottin and Mike Ploog.*

(Bob Villard).

assimilate other forms of life, since the special effects available at the time couldn't do justice to a shape-shifting extra terrestrial. Their representation of Campbell's creature was little more than *Gunsmoke*'s James Arness in a boilersuit with rubber claws and a bald cap.

Three decades later, however, when Carpenter signed on to direct Universal's $15,000,000 remake, technology had evolved sufficiently for Carpenter and his screenwriter Bill Lancaster to return to the book. "I knew that you had to commit one way or the other on the look of the Thing," recalls Carpenter, director of *Halloween* (1978), *The Fog* and *Escape from New York* (1981) and a long-time fan of the Hawks-produced original. "You either had to do what they did on the first one, which is never really see this creature up close, keep him in long shot or shadow, and suggest things. Or you expose the creature to fluorescent lights, and really try to convince the audience that this monster is moving around, doing things and changing. A lot of horror movies up to that point had always ended up with the monster being a man in a suit. Even in *Alien*, as well done as it was, in the end there is one shot where this thing stands up and you realise that it's a big guy in a suit. Great suit. But a *suit*. So the whole point of *The Thing* was to say, 'Let's do the grandaddy of all monsters, let's really *show* this *thing*.'"

To create this "grandaddy of all monsters", Carpenter called upon Rob Bottin, still basking in the media spotlight trained upon *The Howling*. Bottin had also provided a number of post-production shock effects for *The Fog* and had even played the leader of the film's ghostly lepers, Captain Blake. "I talked to a lot of different people," remembers Carpenter, "and Rob was the only guy who came in and said, 'Look, the Thing can be *anything*. It can look like anything. It doesn't have to look like the Creature from the Black Lagoon or Dracula. It doesn't have one

(Bob Villard).

look, it has millions. The idea being that throughout the universe it's been imitating various lifeforms and carries all this information with it. That made a lot of sense to me. The issue then was to design each version of the monster as it went along, with little bits and pieces of what it had imitated before, until, finally, it stands up.

"Rob brought along some film of a test he had done two days before, which was amazing. He had done it with a Christmas ball and a glove, and yet here was this hideous creature. And I thought, 'Let's go with him.' It was just an instinct. It's like how you choose an actor. An actor comes in and you think, 'That's the person that I saw playing that part.' So hiring Rob was a lot like casting."

Initially Bottin was reluctant to commit to what would be his first big budget studio picture. However, after artist Dale Kuipers, who Carpenter had originally hired to design the creature, bowed out through health reasons, Bottin was approached again. This time he agreed. "Dale had come up with something that was a lot better than *Alien*'s face-hugger," says Bottin, "but it was basically a big bug. It was really neat, but it wouldn't be spooky enough. To me, because of the title, I expected something a little more like a *thing*." Having abandoned Kuipers' concept, Bottin, working with illustrator Mike Ploog (and later Mentor Huebner), spent months thrashing out various ideas of his own for the shape-shifting creature. "I didn't want it to remind anyone of any monster they had ever seen. I wanted to avoid, if possible, all the clichés." Hired initially to provide the film's live action storyboards, Ploog, a former comic book artist who has brought his design skills to *Wizards* (1978), *Caveman* (1981), *Heavy Metal* (1981), *The Dark Crystal* (1983) and *Little Shop of Horrors* (1986), was soon roped in to help conceptualise the creature's many states of being. While he left the production midway through principal photography to work on *Superman III* (1983), Ploog was highly influential in both the ultimate look and tone of the film, and Bottin's creations. "We didn't inhibit ourselves with the practicality of it," says Ploog. "You can't come up with something great and different if you're concerned with how you're going to have to do it. You go ahead and come up with something ludicrous, and then you pull back. You depend on people like Rob and his crew to eventually figure it out."

With an initial budget of $750,000 that eventually doubled, and a crew of forty, twenty-four year-old Bottin spent more than a year on the project. Since the vast majority of the effects work would be picked up in post-production, the design of the creature wasn't locked down before shooting began. "What we had was this evolving creature all the way through that kept surprising all of us," says Carpenter. "We would have certain interacting special effects that would go with the sets, based upon certain designs that Rob had,

This page: *The dog-thing, a puppet made by Stan Winston for Bottin.*

which, of course, changed. So we'd shoot something with the entire crew crawling around and then, all of a sudden, it would be another kind of monster. It was a nightmare, but we managed to make it work." When principal photography was completed, the production moved to a warehouse in the San Fernando Valley where all *The Thing*'s effects were filmed over a six-month period.

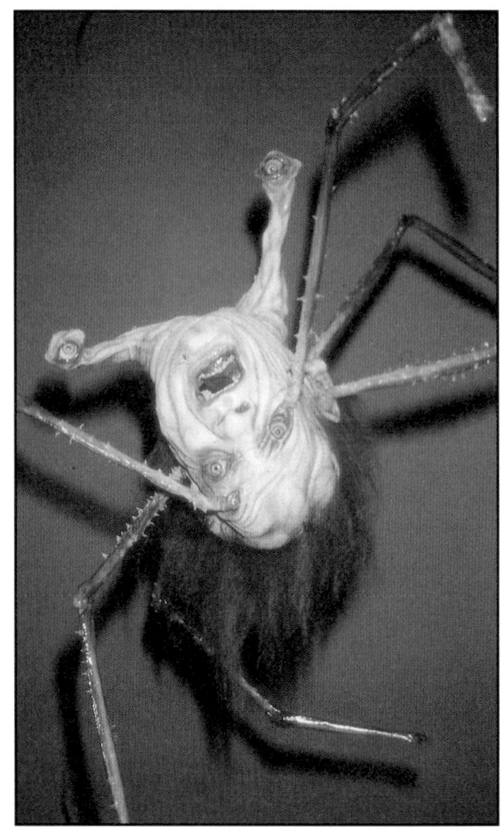

(Bob Villard).

Right and below: *The Norris head, remade (the original having been incinerated in the film) for a cover shoot for* Cinefantastique.

Carpenter manages to keep his monster effectively underwraps for only half an hour — unusual in monster movie terms, but, considering the sheer volume of rubber on display, not that surprising — teasing the audience with glimpses of Bottin's handiwork and generating a palpable sense of paranoia. Then all hell breaks loose. After unwittingly taking in the alien organism, members of a US Antarctic outpost find themselves at the mercy of the body-absorbing extra terrestrial, which first manifests itself when a husky, that is plainly not what it seems, is removed to the camp's dog compound. The other dogs immediately sense something is not quite right, a feeling confirmed moments later when its face splits open and it mutates into a hideous, bloody, writhing mass of twisted flesh and wrig-

(Bob Villard).

Left: *Many versions of Norris' head were constructed by Bottin and his crew.*
Below left: *The Norris-thing writhes about to divert attention from its other head.*

gling tentacles. By the time the alarm is raised the dog has shed its skin and pulled itself up to the compound's ceiling by two gigantic claws (worn by Bottin) which burst from its back.

The scene utilised the talents not only of Bottin but also mechanical effects supervisor Roy Arbogast, who built a number of the life-like huskies, and Stan Winston, whom Bottin brought in to construct the skinless dog-thing that can be seen thrashing about in the kennel once the husky splits apart.

While bizarre and unsettling, it is by no means the film's most startling effect. That honour goes to the one which follows the apparent death of Norris (played by Charles Hallahan) from a heart attack. As Richard Dysart's Doc tries to revive him with cardiac massage, Norris' chest splits open to reveal a set of gnashing teeth which devour the Doc's arms. A marvellous piece of misdirection, the effect was achieved by having a double amputee, wearing a Dysart face mask and gelatine arms, stand in for the actor. When the jaws clamp shut, one instinctively looks at the bloody stumps and not to the actor's face.

Then, from out of the chest bursts another of Bottin's creations, this one bearing a distorted likeness of Norris, which attaches itself to the ceiling. But the best is still to come. "I thought, psychologically, if I was this creature what I'd

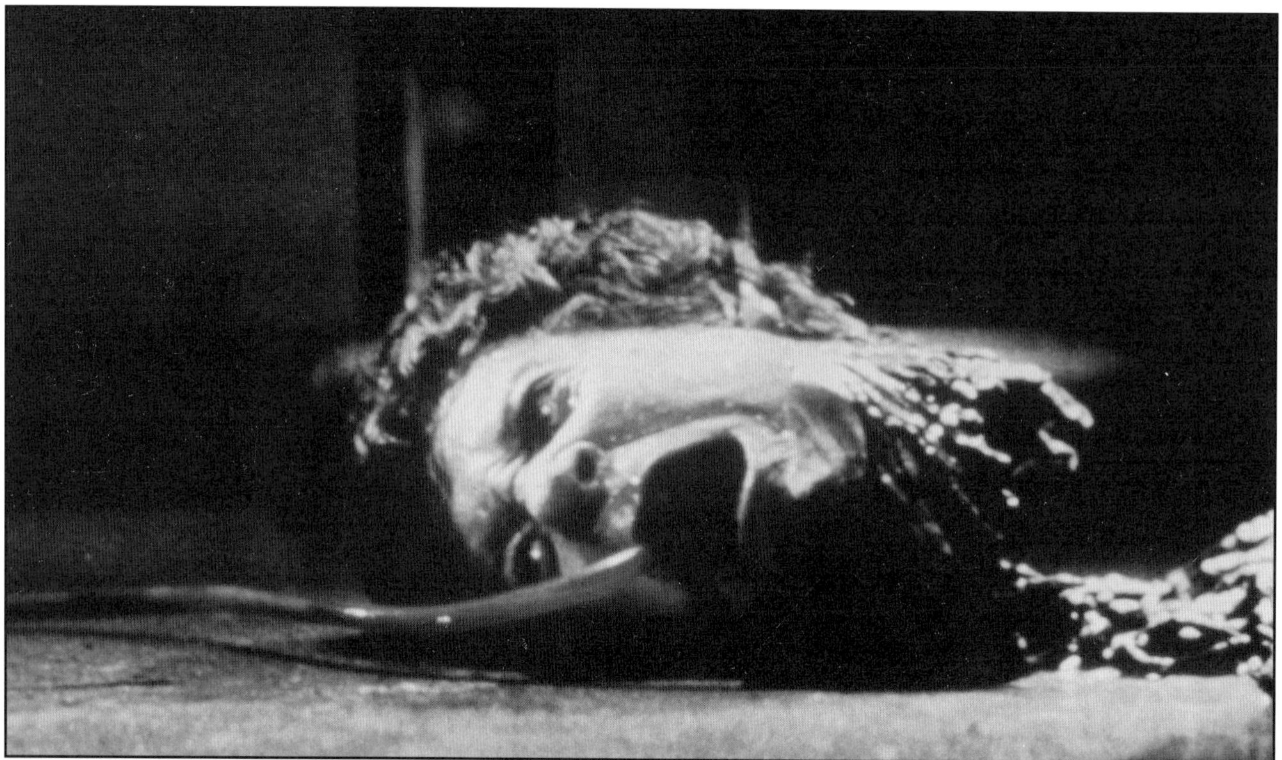

***Top:** A radio-controlled Norris head attempts to make its escape.* ***Above:** This version of the Norris-thing was puppeteered through a hole in the ceiling, while its facial movement was radio-controlled.*

have to do is send out some sort of decoy to get their attention off the part of me that's going to split the room," explains Bottin of his rationale behind the rest of the eye-popping transformation that both he and Ploog admit was heavily influenced by the pulp magazines of the twenties and thirties as well as the E.C. Comics of the fifties. "Then I thought a really fun thing to do would be for Norris' head to escape the room. So the neck stretches, stretches, stretches, until finally it severs and the skin breaks, and you see all this stuff like asparagus stretching, and goo popping. And then the head oozes down the side of the table and drops onto the floor."

While everyone's attention is focused on the Thing on the ceiling, the disembodied head lashes out a whip-like tongue and drags itself under a desk. "Then, to escape the room, it was a case of 'I need some legs quick, and another set of telescopic eyes so I can peep around corners,'" explains Bottin. "So I had spider legs grow out the ears, nose and back of the head." Once equipped with its new legs, it scuttles away to the astonishment of both cast and audience.

"Everybody really came through on the Norris transformation," says Carpenter, "the lighting, the angles, the movement. For that sequence we used every single camera trick you can imagine, and it's a result of the most successful collaboration between writer, director and make-up effects artist. That's the one that we *really* worked on."

"There's no mystery to most of this stuff," admits Bottin. "Most of the techniques are obvious if you think about it. We used cables, servos, pneumatics, hydraulics, hand puppets, wires, radio controls, marionettes, even a little reverse filming. Probably every effect known to man is in this movie."

"The ratio of ideas we had to what we had on the screen was just enormous," says Carpenter, who ultimately excised more than a third of the effects shot from his final cut, including an entire sequence featuring the death of Nauls, the film's roller-skating chef, at the hands (and claws) of the 'Blairmonster', the final manifestation of the Thing which took an incredible *sixty* people to operate. Some effects were removed because the cumulative effect of so many startling sequences was thought to be just too much for audiences to cope with; others because they simply didn't work. "Rob would try to say, 'It's gonna look just like *Outer Limits*. It's gonna be great,'" says Carpenter. "And sometimes it *was* great, and sometimes you'd say, 'What am I making? This is dogshit. Look at this stuff. It's awful.' We'd show up and there would be this strange foam rubber looking thing. And I'd realise we can't shoot this. This doesn't make any sense. And sometimes you'd show up and see this little head crawling on the floor. That entire sequence actually looked like what we had drawn. So it was hit or miss."

Indeed, Carpenter feels that not all the effects that finally made it into the finished cut were entirely successful: "During the blood test scene when Palmer transforms into something that goes up on the ceiling, if you think about it, there is no transformation. We shot it and it was a bunch of balloon-looking stuff, and there is still a shot in there of this kind of strange, pulsating face. But by that point, everybody's so messed up, emotionally, it doesn't matter."

Although Bottin was given an unprecedented amount of control over how his effects were shot, according to Carpenter he often ran into conflict with the film's director of photography, Dean Cundey: "If you look at *The Howling*, you'll see they shot it in a room with venetian blinds. There was a lot of side, cross and backlight, which Rob feels comfortable with, because you don't ever show the rubber. And Dean's concern was, 'Let's put it under the light and bring it to life.' That was our whole idea. So we did. We put it under, for the most part, hard light and it held up. Rob just wanted to be safe. I understand. I would too."

Another of Bottin's and Carpenter's concerns was the amount of blood that would be seen onscreen, with both aware that too much gore during *The Thing*'s transformation sequences would turn moviegoers off. "At previews, people just couldn't take the images," recalls Carpenter. "They saw foetuses, wounds, death and stuff. We used a gooey substance, used in Twinkies, and that's what the slime is, that's what makes the creatures glisten. In some cases we would colour it, and the choice was, 'Should we make it an outer space colour like purple or yellow? Or do we make it what it is, which is bloody?' We went bloody, and whooah what a reaction!"

Though *The Thing* was both a commercial and critical failure at the time of its release — it was, after all, released the same summer as Spielberg's *E.T.*, whose representation of a visiting extra terrestrial was the complete antithesis of Carpenter's — the film has since been acknowledged as a classic of its kind. Moreover, Bottin's stunningly surreal visuals remain, more than a decade later, *the* benchmark against which other make-up effects transformations must be judged.

"It is very difficult to make this stuff work," admits Carpenter. "You do it with a combination of soundtrack, lighting, camera moves, in addition to all the people who are pulling cables and moving things around to make the creature work. We tried a little of everything. And I must give it to Rob, he came up with some really incredible designs. They came right out of his fevered brain. He was influenced by Big Daddy Roth, the guy in the fifties and sixties who drew cartoons of people with giant heads, swollen out of all proportion, driving hot rods. And if you watch his work in *Twilight Zone: The Movie*, you'll see that influence carried to its grotesque extreme." ■

***Below:** Rob Bottin with the most imaginative monster seen in the history of cinema.*

(Bob Villard).

Chapter Seven

You wanna see something really scary?

Rob Bottin: From Twilight Zone to Explorers

Following his astonishing work on *The Thing*, Rob Bottin renewed his association with director Joe Dante for his segment of the Steven Spielberg/John Landis-produced *Twilight Zone: The Movie*, a four-part anthology based on Rod Serling's seminal sixties television series. A reworking of Jerome Bixby's 'It's a Good Life' episode, Dante's highly stylised, comic-horror show starred Jeremy Licht as Anthony, a cartoon-obsessed twelve year-old with the ability to make his every wish, no matter how bizarre, come true.

Opposite top: *The second manifestation of the television creature, and the only one to be shot on set with the actors.*
Opposite bottom: *Rob Bottin, director Joe Dante and Bottin's rabbit creation on the set of* Twilight Zone: The Movie.
Left: *The fourth manifestation of the creature that bursts from the television set in* Twilight Zone: The Movie, *Bottin's homage to the cartoons of Tex Avery.*

Right: *The third version of the television creature was equipped with inflating eyes and a lolling tongue.* ***Far right:*** *Bottin's assistant, Vince Prentice, applying finger prosthetics for the third television creature.* ***Below and bottom:*** *Bottin puppeteers the fifth of the television creatures. Although filmed, it never appeared in the finished film.*

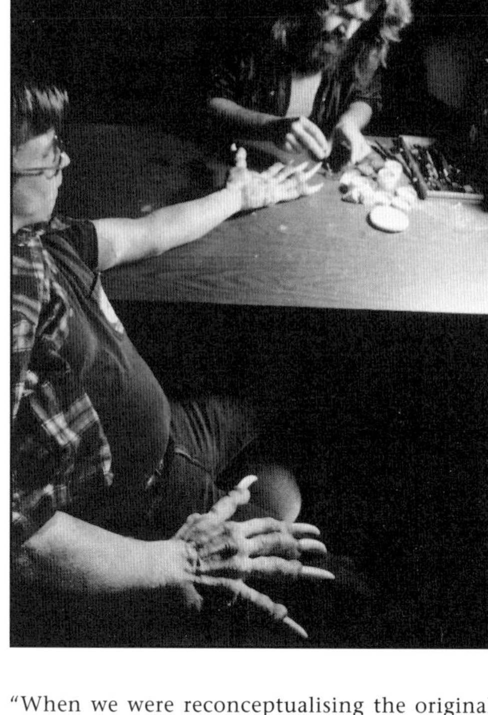

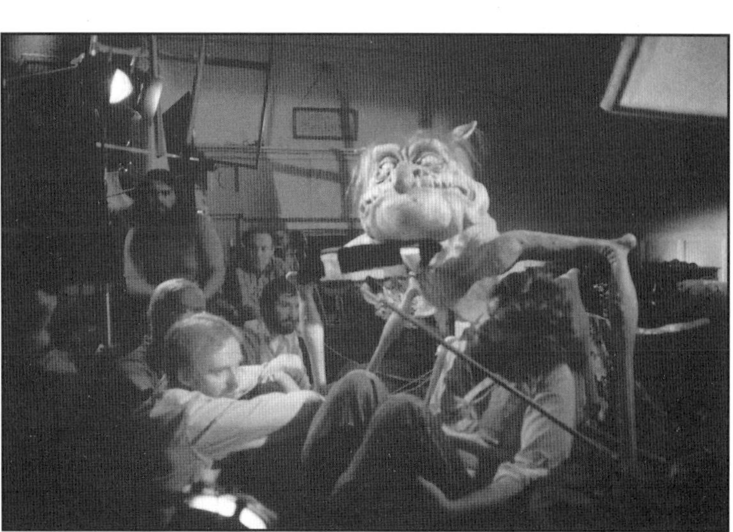

"When we were reconceptualising the original story, we decided to go for the cartoon approach, and that more or less dictated the style of the monsters Rob was going to create," explains Dante. "But Rob, being a fan of Big Daddy Roth, took a lot of inspiration from him, as well as the Tex Avery cartoons we had him watch."

The first real evidence of Anthony's abilities is seen during an impromptu birthday party when his hapless Uncle Walt (Kevin McCarthy) is forced to play the magician and pull a grotesque, hairless rabbit from a top hat. For the trick, a favourite of both Dante and Bottin, the latter built two versions: the first, an inflatable rabbit, powered by an air cannon, that shoots out of the hat; the second, a partially mechanised creature, controlled by rods and cables, that wobbled and snarled.

"Joe said he wanted something creepy, not disgusting like the stuff in *The Thing*, but not funny like a cartoon," explains Bottin. "The idea was to come up with a sinister, sneaky, evil-looking rabbit."

Later, Anthony demonstrates his unique powers by conjuring up a succession of creatures from his television set. "We did five creatures, all of which were supposed to be variations of the same character," Bottin explains. "I came up with one basic creature which had small ears and a big snozzle, and then just took it to its extremes."

The first manifestation bursts forth from the TV and speeds towards camera, contained within a whirlwind — an effect which pays homage to Chuck Jones' Tasmanian Devil. As Dante cuts

ROBOCOP'S ROBOSUIT

To create RoboCop's suit, Rob Bottin spent many weeks trying to pin down the design, going through a large number of sketches before he and director Paul Verhoeven were satisfied.

The suit was sculpted over a body cast of actor Peter Weller, with a special clay used in automotive design, which, due to its ability to stay moist for long periods, can be shaped to a machined finish. In fact, Bottin wanted RoboCop to look like it had stepped out of a car showroom.

The various outer body parts (arms, legs, chest and back) were moulded in silicone rubber and cast in a semi-rigid polyurethane material.

RoboCop's inner suit was made from foam latex and coloured black, and extended from below the ribs to the groin. The rigid, metallic-looking outer pieces were then attached to this inner harness using a combination of Velcro and snap fasteners.

In all, seven suits were manufactured, including a number for stunt use, while others reflected the battle damage that RoboCop suffered throughout the film.

Topped off with a fibreglass helmet, the RoboCop suit ended up weighing forty pounds. Shooting took place in Dallas, Texas, during the summer and the temperatures inside the suit constantly reached 115 degrees, causing Peter Weller to lose several pounds every day. ■

Above: *Director Paul Verhoeven confers with Peter Weller, encased in Rob Bottin's RoboCop suit.*

between his actors and Bottin's work, the creature undergoes a series of bizarre transformations. The second manifestation takes a deep breath, puffs out its cheeks and blows a stream of gas into the face of Kevin McCarthy. Creature number three meanwhile is a simple rod and cable operated puppet, supplemented by a member of the crew, kneeling in front, wearing clawed hands which he wiggles about in shot. But it's the final manifestation, with its dropping jaw, popping eyes and smoke shooting out of its nose and ears, that is the most Tex Avery-like.

Bottin's fifth creature was filmed but later cut, since Dante felt it didn't quite match the look of the other four stages. Essentially a big mouth on legs, it resembles one of Bottin's unused designs for *The Thing*, as realised by Mike Ploog.

"Rob's work on *Twilight Zone* is amazing," enthuses Dante. "I mean, it wasn't a very expensive movie and he really came through with some amazing things."

For Ridley Scott's *Legend*, Bottin produced two of cinema's most memorable make-up effects creations: Tim Curry's eight foot tall, twin-horned epitome of evil, Darkness, and the water-witch Meg Mucklebones (Robert Picardo), who rises from a swamp and bizarrely flirts with Tom

Cruise's wood sprite Jack, before trying to eat him. Ostensibly a less complicated film in terms of make-up effects than *The Thing*, *Legend* was, in fact, much more demanding, since William Hjortsberg's script required a large number of principal characters to wear complicated prosthetic make-up throughout the film.

Bottin originally wanted Darkness' face to appear cat-like, a concept that would have required Curry to wear a combination of prosthetics and mechanics, thus obscuring his own eyes. But while Curry was willing to wear any amount of rubber, he wasn't prepared to have his eyes covered. And so Bottin, who had been approached by Scott to work on *Blade Runner* (1982) but had to decline due to his commitment to *The Thing*, revised the design, taking inspiration from the animated devil in the 'Night on Bald Mountain' sequence from Disney's classic *Fantasia* (1940).

Portraying Darkness meant Curry had to have every part of his upper body covered by foam appliances. "It was physically very uncomfortable," says the actor. "I had prosthetic make-up from the waist up and was in make-up for six or

seven hours a day." Initially the ten piece make-up took eight hours to apply, a process that was later reduced to five-and-a-half. Added to that, Curry wore stilts, as well as three foot long horns which, understandably, put a severe strain on his neck. "Playing Darkness was one of the hardest things I've ever done," he admits.

In addition to Darkness and Meg, Bottin had to create several goblins, including Pox (a pig-faced creature), Blix (a green Keith Richards-lookalike) and two humorous dwarf-like characters named Screwball and Brown Tom. "From a technical standpoint the film's greatest challenge was the elaborate nature of the make-up," opines Bottin. "*Legend* probably had the largest make-up crew ever dedicated to one project."

Left: *Cork Hubbert as Brown Tom from* Legend.
Opposite top: *An alternative concept for Darkness. This make-up was equipped with fluorescent eyes and finger nails. It can only be seen in the American cut of* Legend.
Opposite bottom left: *Rob Bottin's Darkness, a tour de force of prosthetic design.*
Opposite bottom right: *Actor Tim Curry as Darkness enjoys a break from shooting.*
Below: *The Keith Richard-inspired Blix.*

Having completed make-up chores in England on *Legend*, Bottin flew back to America, sketching designs for Joe Dante's *Explorers* en route. As scripted by Eric Luke, Dante's delightful flight of fantasy starred Ethan Hawke, Jason Presson and the late River Phoenix as teenagers who experience a series of strange dreams, leading them to build the spacecraft with which they launch themselves out into the void. There they encounter those responsible for their visions, a pair of bug-eyed, goofy-looking brother and sister aliens named Wak and Neek.

"Wak had such a great personality in the script that I thought that it would be even funnier if he looked kind of dopey and clumsy, but still had a lot of charm and character," recalls Bottin, who took Dante's original concept for the aliens — that of spheres with antennae and eyes stuck on top on them — to imaginatively wild extremes. Since the script called for both Wak and Neek to speak a considerable amount of dialogue, with Wak also having a song and dance number to contend with, Bottin dismissed the notion of using mechanical puppets *à la Twilight Zone* and *The Thing* early on. Instead, he opted for the man-in-the-suit approach, a decision that initially caused Dante some concern. Having convinced Dante of its viability, Bottin cast around for suitable actors to play his creations, settling on Leslie Rickert for the Betty Boop-inspired Neek, with the ubiquitous Robert Picardo as not only Wak but

Right: *One of Bottin's most outlandish designs, Neek, the amorous alien from* Explorers. ***Below:*** *Bob Picardo as Wak performs a song and dance routine in* Explorers.

also Wak's father, a blue-collar alien who turns up to scupper his kids' plans and reclaim the spaceship they have borrowed.

Again, much like his original concept for Darkness, Bottin intended to distort the human form by placing mechanical eye-stalks on top of his actors' heads which would then be blended into appliances on their faces. Fine in theory, it proved problematic in practice, particularly for Picardo who suffered greatly due to the sheer weight of the mechanics inside the father's head-piece. Considerably larger than that of Wak's, it needed to be supported by a mechanical brace. "Bob Picardo deserves a lot of credit for the way he played that stuff," observes Dante, "particularly the father, because the head was so heavy. It had to be held up on wires because his neck couldn't support the weight. It was like wearing typewriters on your head. If the wires had broken, it would have killed him. It was a very tense thing to have to shoot.

"When I'm working with any of these guys — Rick or Rob — I like to let them have their heads. You have to give them freedom to do what they like to do. You can rein them in if it looks like it's going to be too expensive or too impractical — which often happens — but I'm not in a position to dictate to them how I want something to look. I can tell them if I don't like it, but I like to let them come up with their own designs, and have free rein to run rampant with their ideas. But where all this stuff comes from, I don't know. It's the genius factor." ■

TOTAL RECALL SPLITTING HEAD

When Arnold Schwarzenegger's character Doug Quaid arrives on Mars in Paul Verhoeven's *Total Recall* he's disguised as a fat lady. When questioned by the authorities, however, his disguise malfunctions, revealing itself to be an elaborate mechanical mask which splits open to reveal Schwarzenegger inside.

To create this effect, Rob Bottin had to lifecast an actress whose body was large enough to believably contain Schwarzenegger's bulky form, and came across Priscilla Allen. Ultimately, Allen didn't prove to be large enough, and so both her head and body casts had to be enlarged to accommodate Bottin's design.

Using Allen's head cast, Bottin produced a rigid plastic likeness of the actress which would split open on cue to reveal an animatronic puppet head of Schwarzenegger, fitted with mechanical eyes and a flexible neck operated by cables off camera. To complete the illusion, Bottin fitted a mechanism in the splitting head so that its eyes moved as it opened. ■

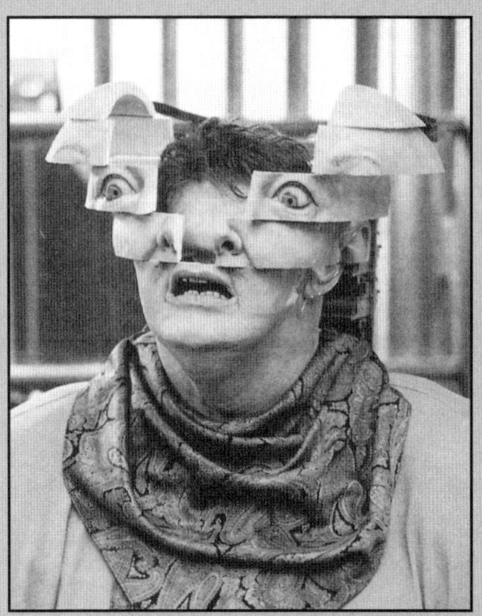

This page: *The head splitting sequence from* Total Recall.

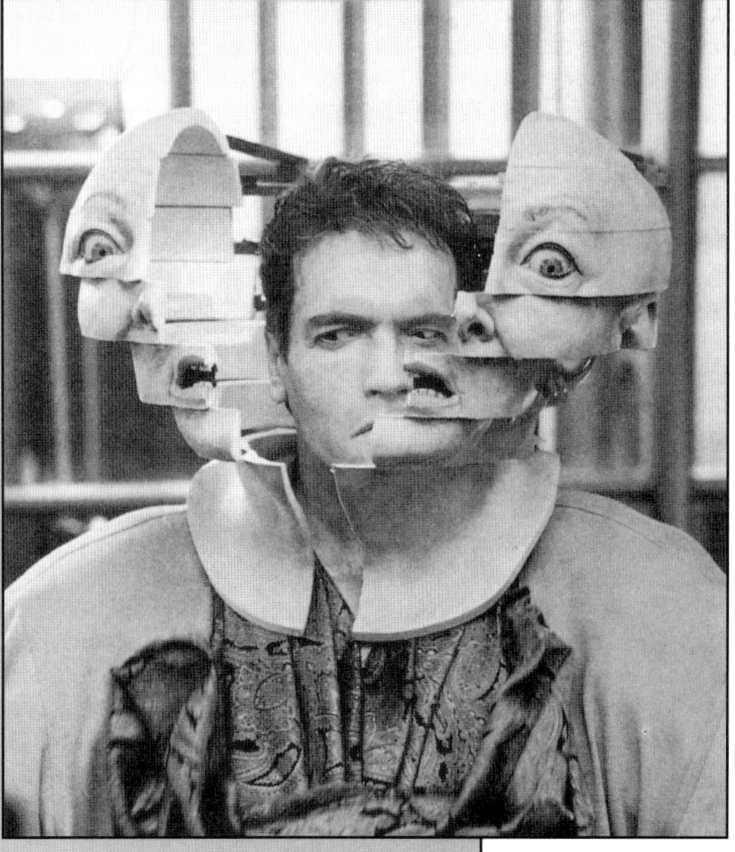

Chapter Eight

Robert Picardo – the man behind the mask

Robert Picardo Interviewed

Robert Picardo has probably worn more rubber than any man alive. As Rob Bottin's favourite 'victim', he has donned several of the heaviest and most extensive prosthetic appliances ever inflicted upon an actor. Beginning with the role of Eddie Quist in *The Howling*, Picardo followed that by playing the water witch Meg Mucklebones in Ridley Scott's *Legend*, Wak the bug-eyed alien and his equally bug-eyed father in *Explorers*, as well as providing the voice and likeness for Johnny Cab in *Total Recall* (1990). On Broadway, Picardo starred opposite Jack Lemmon in the acclaimed *Tribute* and has never found himself wanting of straight roles; he has had regular spots on TV's *The Wonder Years* and *China Beach*, and also appeared in Dante's *Gremlins 2 The New Batch* (1990), *InnerSpace* and *Matinee* (1993). 'Rubber shows' are only taken on when he feels he can invest the latex with character.

"After *The Howling* Rob decided that I was an actor who would put up with their shit and he could count on me to go through the grinds of the make-up session and still perform. I don't think a lot of actors realise that it not only takes

Opposite: *Bottin transforms Picardo into Meg Mucklebones for Ridley Scott's* Legend.
Left: *Picardo's first outing with prosthetics — as Eddie Quist in* The Howling.

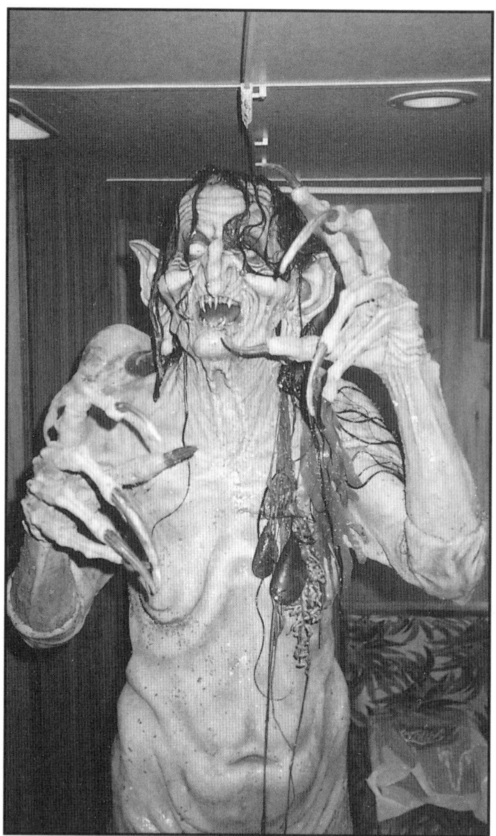

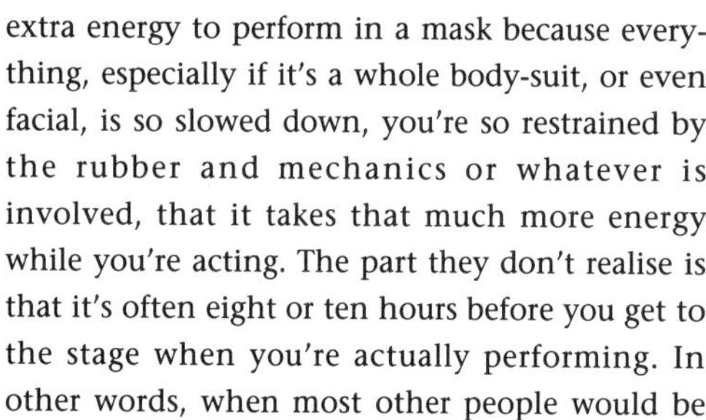

extra energy to perform in a mask because everything, especially if it's a whole body-suit, or even facial, is so slowed down, you're so restrained by the rubber and mechanics or whatever is involved, that it takes that much more energy while you're acting. The part they don't realise is that it's often eight or ten hours before you get to the stage when you're actually performing. In other words, when most other people would be saying, 'Goodbye, I'll see you tomorrow', that's when your day starts, that's when you go to work. So it's a matter of conserving your energy during the course of the day, and resting as much as possible during the make-up stages, so that when the time comes, you can really pour on the energy. Making up *is* tiring because, for most actors, you're a little jazzed when you get to the set, you're ready, you're there to act and you're used to going to work. So even when you get there at 4am and sit in the make-up chair, your mind is going, and you're expending a certain amount of energy just anticipating the day, and getting ready to do the work.

"The day we did the first test for *Explorers*, I got there at four in the morning, and went in front of the camera at 8.30 at night, and during the day I was in preparation. That doesn't mean I was in that stuff all day. They would get a certain amount done, and then they'd have a problem, and they would work on the problem for two to three hours while I had the big rubber hands on, and then they would get the face on, and then they would be feeding me lunch, and then they would have another problem with the mechanics. It was a long day. And what you don't realise is that they've spent however many million dollars on you, and this is the first time they're seeing you, and nobody wants to hear you complaining that you've been there for sixteen-and-a-half hours. They want it to be absolutely magical from the first moment. And certain things didn't work the first day. The cable mechanisms were so restraining, they had this big shank of cable, like a braid, coming out of the back of my head, and they hadn't been properly floated so I could move my head. It was as if someone was clamping my head from behind, and Rob kept saying, 'Move more, move more', but I couldn't. That's why I think Rob liked to count on me, to go to the limit of my ability, with as little complaint as possible.

"For *Legend*, they had to do a whole torso and upper body cast of me. You can only breathe very shallowly. You can't expand your chest and it's very scary. Obviously you can't go to the bathroom. You can't do *anything*. I've had to do that casting process all over the face many times and it's all a matter of mind control. If you start thinking about the fact that you can't breathe or you can't hear, or that everybody could go off and leave you there... If you think about it, it's very disturbing. If you keep your mind busy you can do it a million times. It's really about talking to yourself and remaining calm. Don't remind yourself of the time you got trapped under the house, don't think about being trapped in an elevator. Think about nice things, and play music you enjoy.

"Because Rob is such a perfectionist, he inspires in you the desire to join him in his perfection, meaning you try your hardest for him. He has such a specific thing in mind that you get sort of excited about helping him fulfil it, which is the only way you can put up with the stuff. I mean, I had a legitimate acting career already, so it wasn't like I was doing this as a way of getting into the actors' union."

How did you get the part of Meg Mucklebones in *Legend*?

"I was a whim of Ridley Scott's because he'd seen *The Howling* and liked me. I was hoping to get the role of Darkness, that was the big part, but then they decided to use Tim Curry, who's not only a wonderful actor but he's got one of the best voices going and that was so important in that characterisation. And since everybody else is a little person, the only other full-sized person in the film is the witch.

"Meg's make-up at first took about six-and-a-half hours to put on, but they got that down to around five. I had a wonderful humpback, the arm prosthetics were all glued on, we had Rob's famous finger gloves with a couple of extra joints which had a heavy wire core so you could pose them. And then the torso was basically a suit that

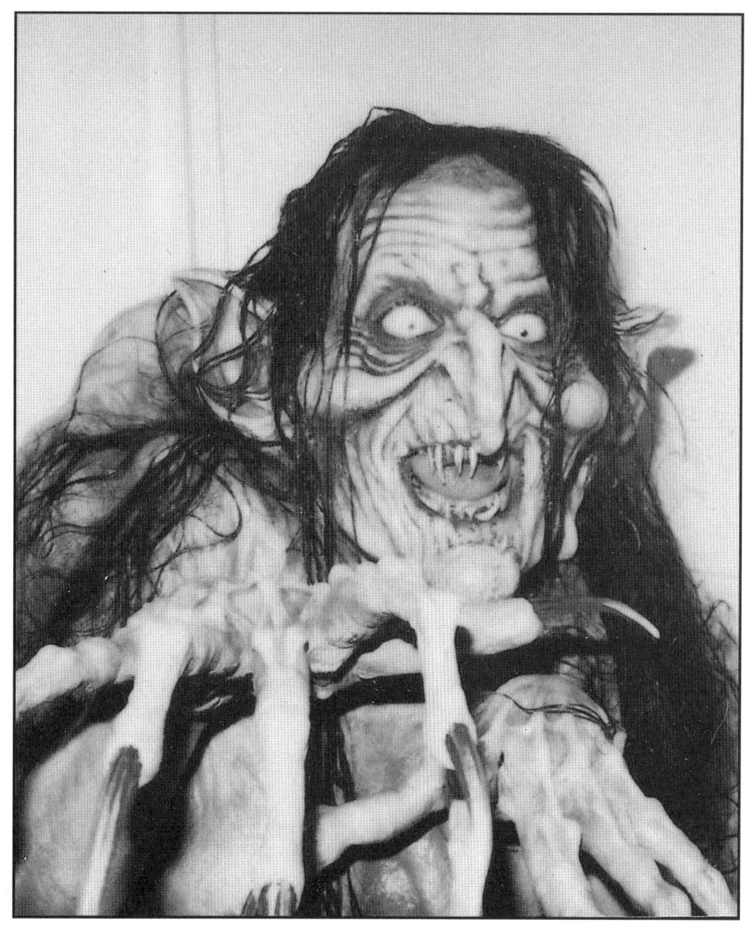

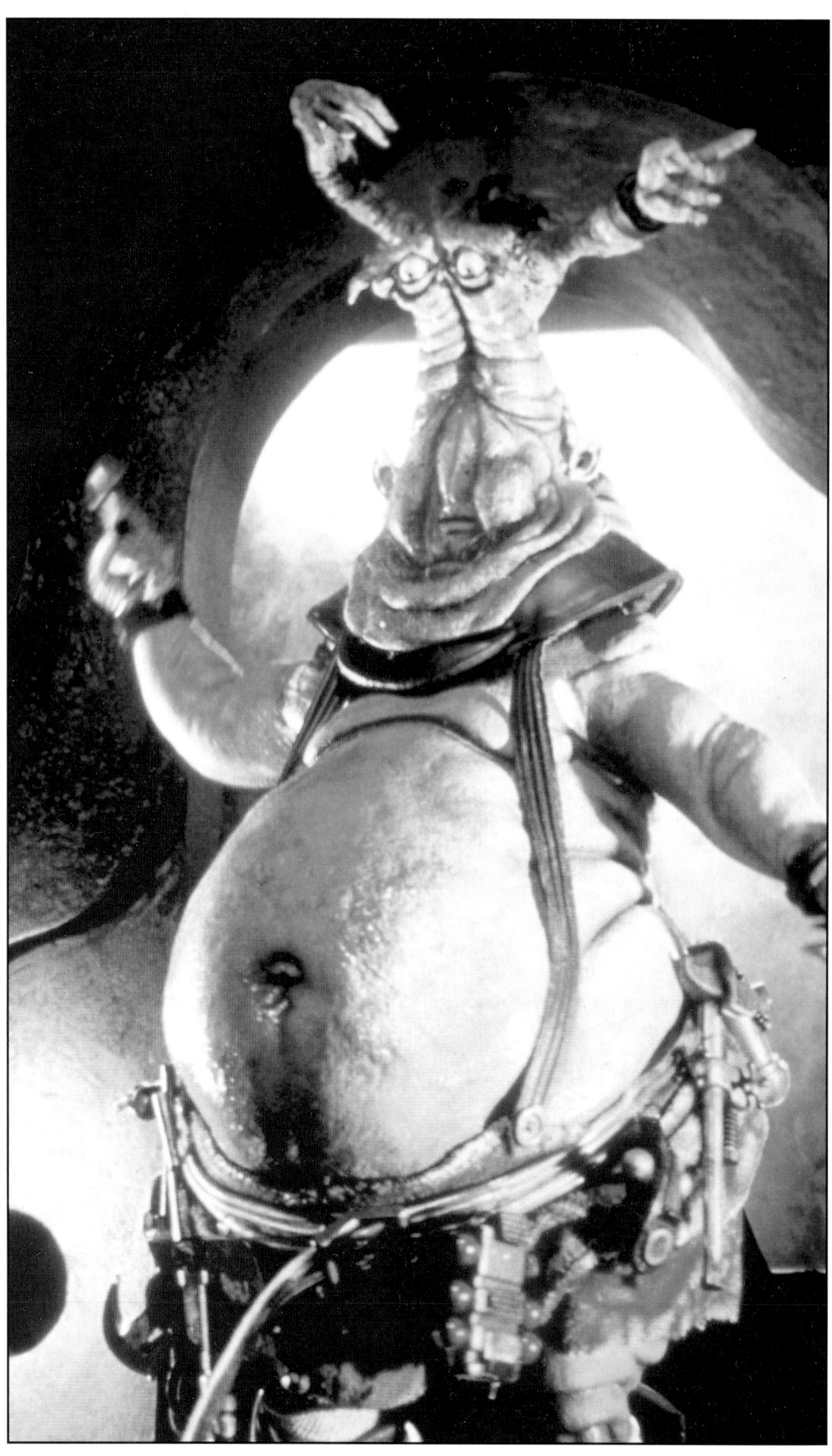

***Right:** The alien father in* Explorers, *Picardo's toughest 'rubber show' to date.*

you stepped into and got zipped up the back. It was built on a very, *very* tight body-stocking. So I would get into this stuff and they would talk to me about how they want me to come up out of the water. Ridley wanted me to come up from an absolutely perfectly still surface. The whole stage was filled with about three feet of water, and I stood on a little trapdoor which would raise me up from below the floor. It wasn't terribly large — about three foot square. I had a platform and a pole that was welded under the trap, with a little cushion in the back that held me right under the butt, or in the small of the back, so that my upper body could swivel. Now, I was wearing a rubber suit, which when it absorbed water weighed about seventy to eighty pounds. It just soaked water up and I had no way to tell them if I was in distress. I said to one of the stunt co-ordinators as they were getting ready to put me on the platform and drop me under the water, 'When you drop me down, when you first push me under, if you push the trap too quickly won't my body recoil? If I recoil back far enough, you could shear my arm off, you could decapitate me.' He went, 'Yes, I suppose you're right.' They arranged some sort of an air-jet right in front of me on the surface that created a pulsating little whirlpool right there that I would hide behind, so I actually started with my face above the water and they would push me up very suddenly. So it ended up working out okay. During the shooting my eyes would be so sensitive from the lenses I had to wear, that even after I took them out I still had to wear dark glasses for the rest of the evening, even when I was sitting inside.

"The suit didn't have feet, but it went all the way down to the ankles. It didn't have legs, I was supposed to have like a long tail. The idea was that this witch was like a kind of giant serpent. Meg is many people's favourite make-up in the movie. There was something about all the folds and the face that made this creature seem so real. There was something a little bit static about the face of Darkness. It is a beautiful sculpture but it doesn't have any movement in the face. With Meg, the impression was that the character was in a constant state of movement. Rob coaches you, he says, 'Show me this, show me that.' He knows how the make-up moves in his mind's eye, so I often exactly mimic what he's asked for. I was very proud of *Legend*, more so than *The Howling*, because *The Howling* was my first outing, and once I saw how extreme I looked, I realised what made the performance interesting was to be extremely relaxed; this made the character much more interesting than being threatening. I don't take a lot of credit for my performance in *The Howling*, I feel it was created for me; the way Joe Dante directed it, the way John Hora lit it and the way that Rob thought through that transformation as being part of the character. In *Legend* I felt I had more to do with the way the character came across.

"You must remember, I am a regular actor. I have a regular actor's career and I take these parts if it seems like I can really make an actor's contribution to the role. Not if you're just a tree standing there and they're putting ornaments on you, but you can actually express yourself through it. I love working with Joe and Rob, and they pay you well. In *Explorers*, I couldn't quite understand why they needed me, but again they ended up paying me handsomely for being the guy in the rubber suit.

***Above:** Bottin's assistant, Greg Cannom, applies bladders to Robert Picardo on* The Howling.

"In *Explorers*, where the characters finally meet Wak for the first time, the make-up wasn't completely ready, there were still problems that had to be solved. So they covered up parts of the suit that didn't quite work, and for the first scene I had this big furry coat on, which was used to cover the parts that weren't finished. When we didn't need it any more I tore it off."

What has been the most difficult make-up you've had to wear?

"The father in *Explorers* took more all-over energy than any I have done because there was so much weight on me. Meg wasn't mechanical, so when I came out of the water there was a lot of extra weight on me. However, as the take went on, the water would just pour out of me, the make-up would get lighter, and so I never thought of it as being hard to move. In *Explorers* it was very, very hard to move everything — my face, my body. And when I did the father make-up, that was ridiculous. The body was really huge, you could literally lift the belly, and drop it about twelve inches. It was *excruciating*. With Wak it was like having a typewriter on my head; for the father it was more like a TV. There was a support behind me; but just because the weight is being partially borne by an armature, you are still turning the whole thing. I got open lesions on my head from that make-up. We did it all in one day and it was just torturous. Every time I turned my head, it was like 'Arrrrggghhh.' After several hours, my head started hurting real bad. It was the only time I have ever cried. When the crew took the second meal break my day at that point had been about twenty hours. I ended up working twenty-one-and-a-half hours that day. They couldn't take the make-up off me, so when the crew had the break I started to cry because I was in absolute agony, and nobody could do anything for me. It was the worst day I have ever had.

"The last thing I did for Rob was *Total Recall* — I was Johnny Cab. For that, Rob just came over to my house and took a series of pictures of me making faces from which to sculpt Johnny. Then I went in and looped the voice."

Would you don rubber again?

"It's a tough call at this point because as you get older it takes an awful lot more energy. I'll only do the rubber role if I get a worthwhile straight part. I hope it would be either a dual role, like the old Jekyll and Hyde transformation, and if it isn't that, then I would get to play two characters. But I've told Rob I definitely have a swansong in me, a swansong to rubber." ■

This page: *Bottin's animatronic puppet of the mutant leader Kuato.* **Opposite top:** *Bottin's reference photo for Johnny Cab.* **Opposite bottom:** *Picardo's caricature likeness as Johnny Cab.*

TOTAL RECALL'S MUTANT KUATO

Two versions of the baby-faced mutant Kuato were produced by Rob Bottin. The first, for long shots, was little more than a prosthetic appliance. Shaped like a large T-shirt which was worn by the actor, Marshall Bell, the piece was blended into Bell's skin under his chin and extended below his waist. Kuato's head and arms, which protruded from the appliances 'stomach', were cable operated by fifteen technicians off-camera. To support both the heavy mechanics and cables, the whole prosthetic was mounted on a parachute harness which spread the weight more evenly.

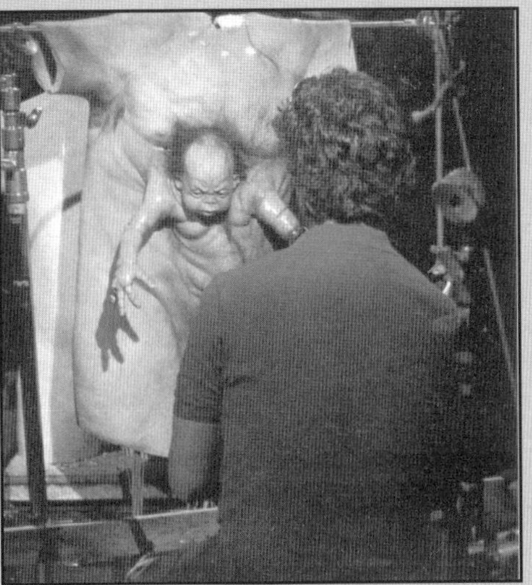

For close-ups of Kuato speaking, not only did Bottin construct a twin fully mechanised version, but also a head-to-hips animatronic Marshall Bell. This puppet Bell was mounted on a wheeled cart, which, when pushed along, moved the figure up and down to simulate walking. The mechanical figure was also equipped with a sophisticated neck movement and bellows to simulate breathing. The arms were controlled by a slave system, allowing everything that the puppeteer's arms did to be duplicated by the puppet.

The animatronic Kuato had fully articulated eyes, eyelids, brow, lip and jaw movement, while its arms were also controlled by a slave system. For the all-important dialogue scenes, Kuato's servo motor driven lips were first made to perform their lines under a puppeteer's control, but with a computer hooked up to record the movements. Once on set, the computer could be made to playback the moves, achieving a flawless take each time. The puppet also had its own set of bellows to make it breathe and, depending on the action required, needed between fifteen and twenty puppeteers to bring it to life. ■

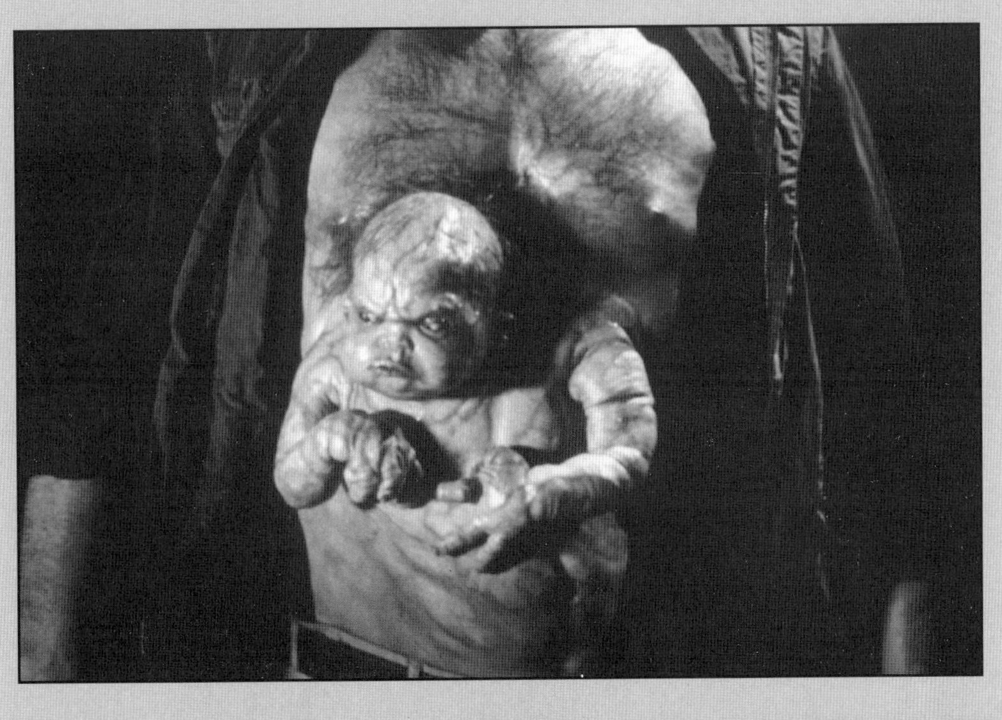

Chapter Nine

From dried apple skins to green garbage guzzlers

The early career of Steve Johnson up to Fright Night

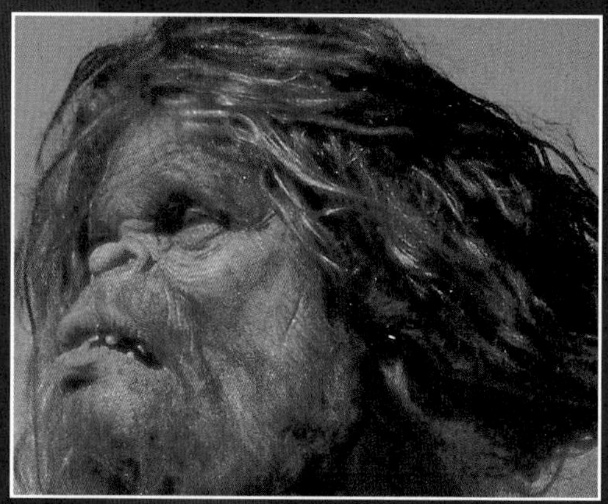

A pivotal member of Rick Baker's team on *American Werewolf*, *Videodrome* and *Greystoke: The Legend of Tarzan Lord of the Apes* (1984), Texas-born Steve Johnson, much like Baker and Bottin before him, had his interest in make-up fuelled by the images he saw in *Famous Monsters*: "For as long as I can remember I have been interested in monster movies and very bizarre things, and I was a creative little kid. In 1972, when I was twelve, make-up effects was not a legitimate thing, it was not something you could point to in a magazine, show your friends or your parents and say, 'This is what I want to do, this is what I'm going to

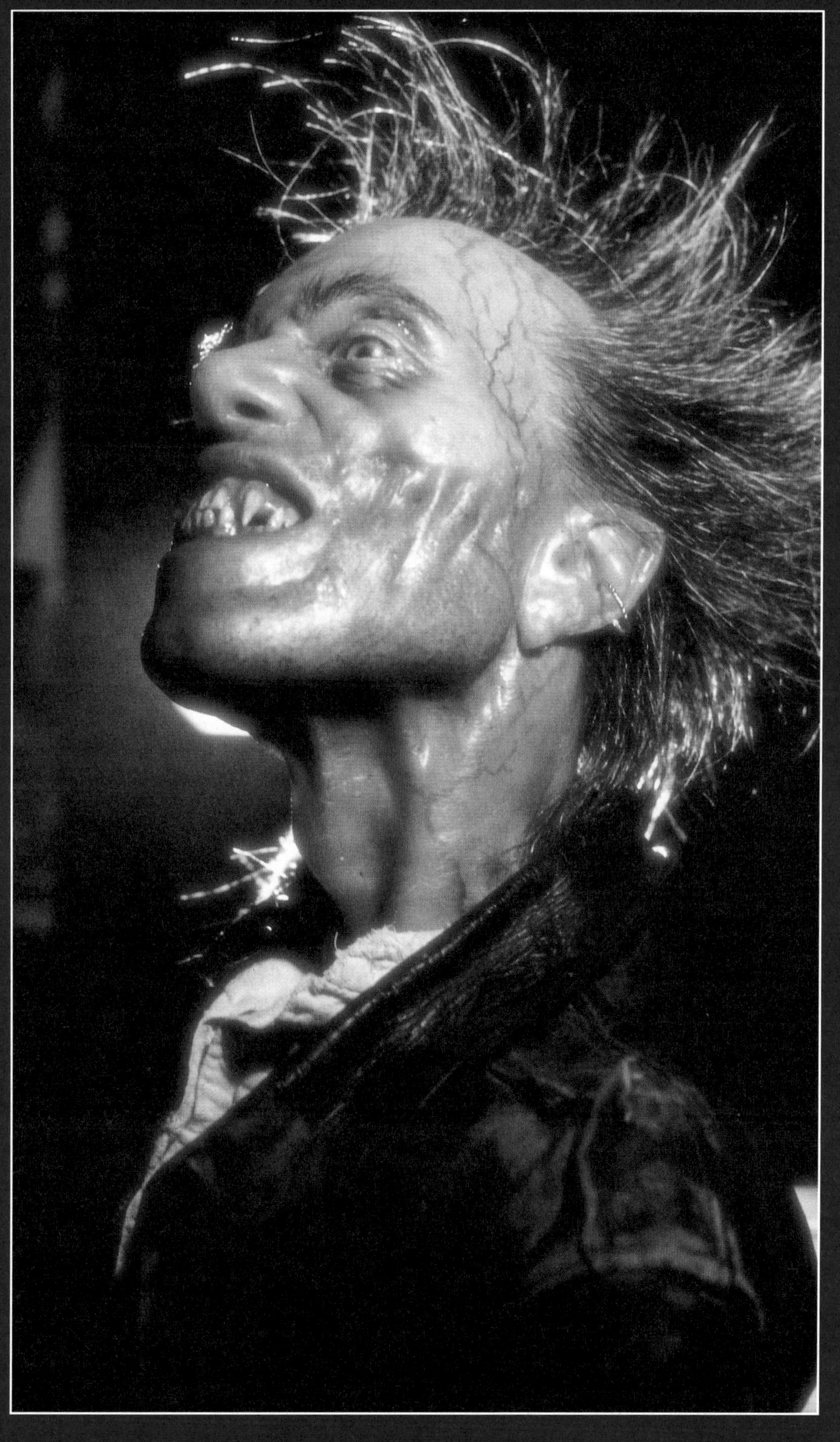

Opposite top: *A Neanderthal make-up.* ***Opposite bottom:*** *A zombie rises from the grave, a personal project of Steve Johnson's.* ***Left:*** *A Johnson head based on a vampire character from* They Thirst, *a novel by Robert R. McCammon.*

crazy. Now I had a handle on professional techniques, not only that, I knew where to get the stuff. I immediately went to the back of the book to do the most complicated make-up — it was a miserable failure. So I was really frustrated for about a day, and then I thought, 'Maybe I should just start with some of the simple ones and go from there.' I started saving every penny I could, sending off to get all the make-up supplies. I was hooked."

Despite the revelatory advice offered by Smith's handbook, Johnson's idol was not the godfather of make-up effects, but his young protégé, Rick Baker. "The thing about Rick was he seemed accessible," explains Johnson. "More importantly, he was a young kid with long hair having fun making monsters. He was in the public eye, he was doing conventions, he was in monster magazines. That was really exciting for another young kid who wanted to do the same thing."

The guiding hand of Rick Baker reached out to Johnson when he was sixteen. Home sick from school one day, he saw Baker on a local television show called *Dialling for Dollars*, wearing a mask he had made for *Star Wars*. Baker, it transpired, was a guest that weekend at a science fiction convention in Houston and Johnson's mum drove her son to meet his idol: "I showed him my little portfolio and he seemed genuinely impressed. And I think he was, if only because here was some kid in the most redneck area of the country doing make-up.

__Top:__ Johnson helped create the graphic demise of Barry Convex in Videodrome *while working for Rick Baker's EFX company.* ***Above:*** *The hand-gun from* Videodrome. ***Right:*** *Originally, Johnson had intended that the library ghost would transform into this beast, but it was decided to limit the change to the photo on the far right.* ***Far right:*** *The library ghost from* Ghostbusters.

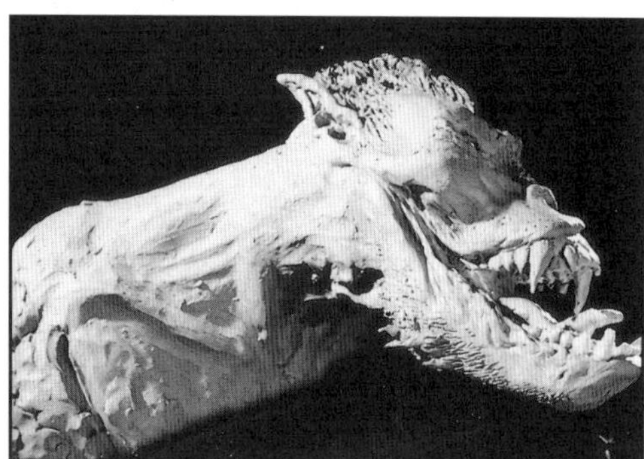

uproot myself for and try to make a living at it.' It was crazy then, I guess *I* was crazy."

Johnson's first attempts at make-up amounted to little more than sticking dried apple skins onto his friends' faces. It wasn't until Johnson saw an advertisement for Dick Smith's *Monster Make-up Handbook* in the back of *Famous Monsters* magazine that his interest solidified: "I lost my mind. I think it was like $1.75, but I didn't have enough, so I went in half with a friend on it, and just went

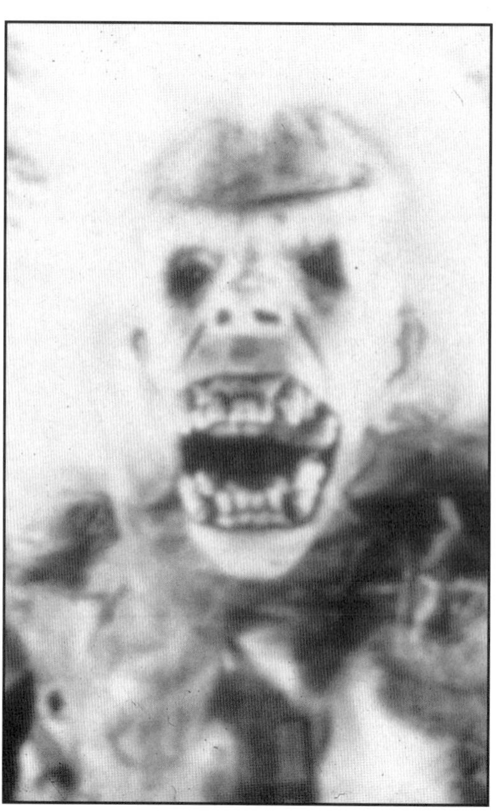

GHOSTBUSTERS' SLIMER EFFECT

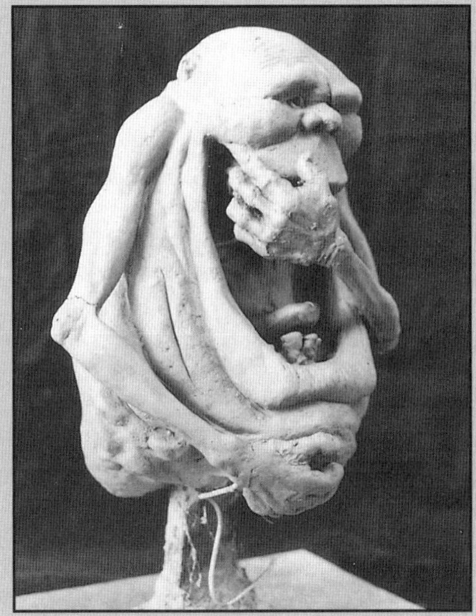

To create Slimer, the voracious green ghoul who appears early on in Ivan Reitman's supernatural comedy *Ghostbusters*, make-up effects supervisor Steve Johnson tried to avoid using any internal mechanics as much as possible, producing something that was effectively "a big squishy puppet", which was then shot against a black background with a series of operators, dressed all in black velvet, puppeteering it from behind.

"The device was a kind of half-mechanical, half-body-suit creation," Johnson reveals. "We designed it so low-tech it was amazing, but that face is just swimming with movement. To make his cheeks move when he's chewing, I had a guy standing with his arms going through slits, grabbing big handles on the inside of his cheeks. You could never move that mass with any cable or motor that I know of; not that quickly and not responsively."

"The jaw was the same thing. I had a big piece of spring metal in the lower lip, on a bar, coming out of the bottom of the puppet. Not only would that open and shut the jaw, and keep the lip real flexible and bouncy, but if you twisted the handle, you got all this really neat stuff, basically for free. And with no under-structure in there, the face could just do crazy things." ■

***Above left:** One of the initial sculpted concepts for Slimer, from* Ghostbusters*.*
***Above right:** Sigourney Weaver reacts, much to Johnson's pleasure, to meeting Slimer.*
***Below:** A finished concept for the Green Ghoul.*

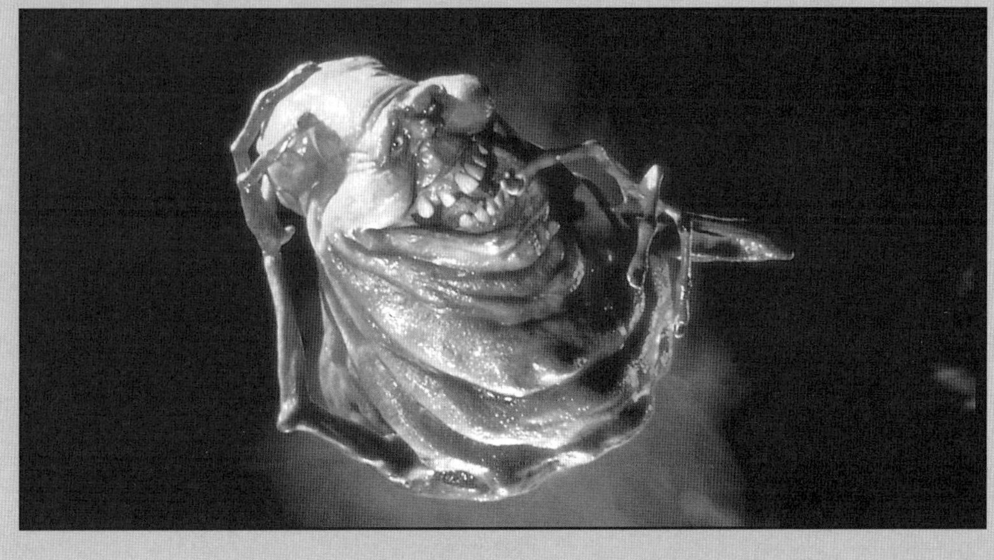

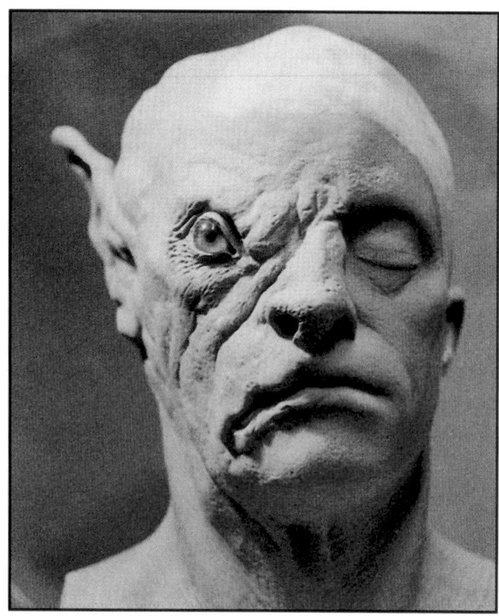

He gave me his phone number and I started corresponding with him. That was a real turning point for me — I wasn't playing any more. I was doing stuff to impress Rick Baker — as a potential employer. He always said, if I moved up to California, he would help me out."

"Steve had a really good portfolio," says Baker, "and I was especially impressed because he was from Texas. If you live in California, the information and supplies are more readily available, but in Texas they're a bit more difficult to come by. Steve's stuff was very good despite that problem."

"Rick was really encouraging, and he was the difference between my deciding whether I was going to do this professionally, or stay in Texas and get into architecture or advertising," reveals Johnson. "There are so many people out there now who send their stuff in, and you can't respond to all of it. I used to think, 'What if Rick had been this way to me? What if he hadn't responded at all?' I wouldn't be here. But it *is* different now. I was maybe one out of ten at that point; these people now are maybe one out of 2,000 — maybe more. But I think a lot of it was Rick's genuine interest, wanting to support someone he felt had potential. When Rick put together the initial crew on *American Werewolf*, he hired people *I* saw no potential in. But after being with Rick for two years, these guys were *incredible*. Rick knew that, he knew they had that potential, they just needed to be guided a little bit."

Johnson left Texas and moved to Los Angeles when he was seventeen to try his luck in movies, enrolling at a local college as insurance should he fail: "I never thought I'd get into this business as quickly as I actually did. I thought perhaps it would take five years, maybe ten, but I was dedicated enough to come and stick it out." Two weeks after arriving in Los Angeles, Johnson got the call from Rick Baker: "He had referred me to Greg Cannom who was doing this silly little low budget film about a bunch of apes. It was a hysterical experience." Following his work on *Galactic Connection* (1977), Johnson collaborated with Rob Bottin on several films, including *Tanya's Island*, *Humanoids from the Deep*, *The Fog*, *The Howling* and *Airplane!* (1980), for which they created Leslie Nielsen's elongating nose effect.

Then Johnson joined Baker's newly formed company, EFX, to work on *An American Werewolf in London*: "*American Werewolf* was the one period of my life that I can describe as pure magic, because I had always respected Rick so much, he was my

Above: *An early make-up concept for an asymmetrical transformation for* Fright Night. ***Below left:*** *Evil Ed turns from wolf to boy in Tom Holland's* Fright Night. ***Below right:*** *A make-up concept for* The Lost Boys.

Far left: *This simple latex mask was made especially for a Japanese book on make-up.*
Left: *Steve Johnson.*
Below: *Johnson sculpting the head of the Great Beast for* Poltergeist 2: The Other Side.

hero. I would go to work early, every day, I'd be so excited, because I was going to be working with Rick Baker. It was just a wonderful period in my life." As part of the seven-strong EFX crew, Johnson sculpted one of the four Nazi demons, helped construct the Jack puppet, and was in charge of moulding and casting all the 'change-o-heads'.

Johnson feels he gained a lot from working with Bottin and Baker: "What I learned from Rob was specifically design. How to really twist something around and not settle for what someone might expect, not settle for something even close to what someone might expect. One day, Shawn McEnroe, Rob and myself wanted to make a zombie, just for fun. We decided to put a time limit on it, make it a contest. I was real excited. But then Rob said, 'No, I've changed my mind, because I know I'll win.' Finally I got him to tell me what he was planning.

"Now, one of the stipulations of the contest was that it had to be a make-up, it couldn't be a puppet. One of Rob's ideas was to backlight his zombie strongly, use a very reflective material in certain areas, and shoot it in such a way that it looked like you were seeing holes through the make-up. He would have won, because he didn't think of it as 'I'm going to do a really cool zombie', he thought of it as 'I'm going to do something that *ensures* it's the *best*.'

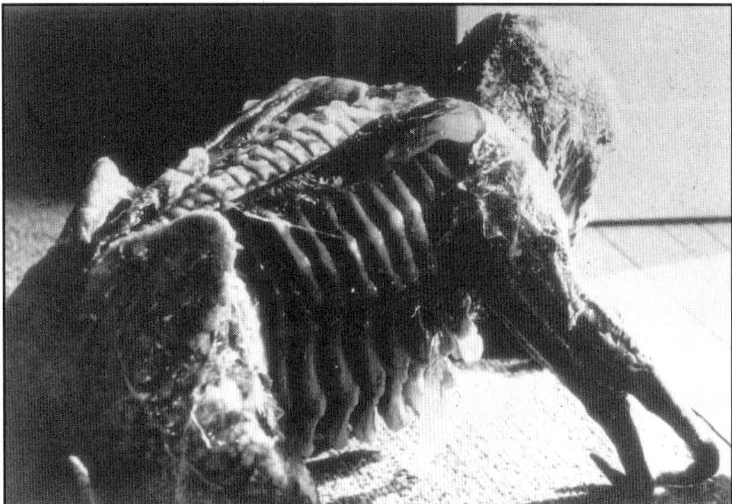

Top: *The wild man from* Big Trouble in Little China. **Above:** *Johnson's Vomit Creature from* Poltergeist 2: The Other Side, *in its final state, scuttles out of the room.* **Right:** *Craig T. Nelson brings up the appropriately named Vomit Creature.*

"With Rick, I never really *knew* what I learned, when I learned it. I knew I was learning how to do things *professionally*, but I just thought it was the way it was done: you make a mould this way, you do sculpture this way, you design something this way. After I left Rick's and began to see other people who had worked for other make-up artists, I saw how they worked, what they thought was finished, what they thought was a good design. It confused me at first, until I realised I learned from the *best*. I went from Greg Cannom through Rob Bottin to Rick Baker. They learned from Rick — so I was constantly learning the best way to do it, which is Absolutely Perfectly Finished. It has to look good to the eye. If it doesn't, it's not going to look good to the camera. That's how I thought it had to be, until I saw that not everyone thought that way. There's a lot of people who don't treat it as an art. But everyone who's learned through Rick does, even if it means not making as much money on a certain project. To me, it's my art. I get satisfaction through producing really good work. The truth is, more often than not, it doesn't matter to the camera. But it matters to me, and it matters to the people on set. If it looks good to them, they're going to remember that."

After wrapping up *American Werewolf*, Baker and his EFX crew began work on David Cronenberg's *Videodrome*, which starred James Woods as a sleazy cable TV producer and pop singer Debbie Harry as his S&M love interest. For this bizarre, hallucinogenic film — the second half of which exists entirely in Woods' head — Baker was called upon to create a series of flesh-twisting horrors, including a rash on Woods' stomach that turns into a vaginal hole, into which he deposits his gun. The effect is repeated when the sinister Barry Convex 'programmes' him with a videotape. Later, when Woods fishes around in his stomach for his gun, he retrieves it, only to discover that it

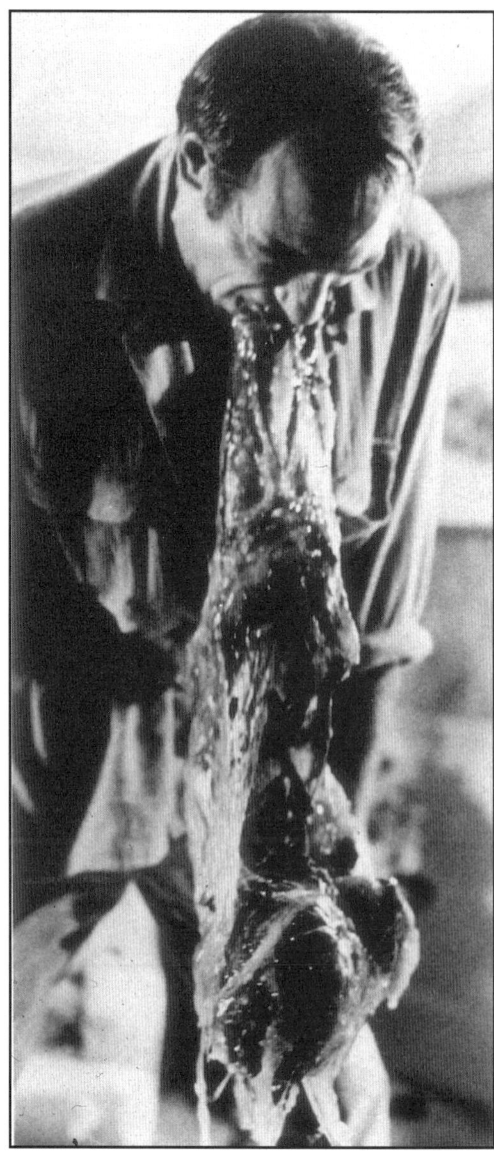

has begun to fuse with his hand to form a *hand-gun*, a fleshy appendage which, in the film's most unsettling scene, is fired at Convex, causing him to burst apart. Baker's crew also constructed a breathing television and a number of breathing video cassettes.

"Originally there was a lot more stuff in the movie," explains Johnson who, together with Dick Smith, cast Debbie Harry's torso for the scene in which a cigarette is stubbed out on her breast and who became Baker's right-hand man during shooting when his employer began pre-production work on EFX's next project, *Greystoke: The Legend of Tarzan Lord of the Apes*. "Debbie Harry's character had one of these vaginal slits in her stomach, and there was also a sex scene, a very explicit sex scene, between Jimmy and Debbie, where her hand turned into a penis and slid up into this weird vaginal orifice on his arm. It never got shot."

Greystoke, Hugh Hudson's epic $40,000,000 adaptation of Edgar Rice Burroughs' famed story, required Baker, Johnson and the rest of the EFX crew to relocate to England for the better part of a year where, together with some forty British technicians and a similar number of wig makers, they set up an ape-factory to produce the film's twenty simian cast members.

On his return to America, Johnson left EFX to head the make-up effects department at Richard Edlund's company, Boss Films: "I had my own building, I hired, I developed everything, I saw it through, I was artistically in charge, but I had nothing to do with the money. I never had to worry about pulling jobs in. There was always a new job waiting, overlapping the last one. There was a real safety net. And I think that helped me a lot in learning to control people and manage budgets."

***Above:** Johnson sculpts a Gigeresque horror for* Poltergeist 2: The Other Side. ***Left:** This monkey-jester was made for a Japanese book on make-up effects.*

Johnson's first job at Boss was the hugely successful Ivan Reitman-directed comedy *Ghostbusters* (1984) on which he was responsible for a number of the film's otherworldly apparitions, including a zombie taxi driver, the librarian ghost who transforms from a sweet-looking bookish old lady into a hideous demon and, perhaps most famously, Slimer, the green garbage-guzzler who the ghostbusters encounter stuffing his face in a hotel corridor.

While at Boss, Johnson created the H.R. Giger-designed Vomit Creature and the multi-tentacled Great Beast for *Poltergeist 2: The Other Side* (1986), as well as a number of elaborate make-up effects for Tom Holland's engagingly old-fashioned comic-horror tale *Fright Night* (1985), including Chris Sarandon's vampire and Stephen Geoffrey's vampiric-wolf Evil Ed. "I had an incredible amount of freedom on *Fright Night*," admits Johnson who remains proud of Evil Ed's transformation from wolf to boy, particularly the stage where Ed is caught mid-transformation: half boy, half wolf. "It was used in the movie in a quick cut, but the concept was really nice." ■

Chapter Ten

This time it's war: the bitch is back!

Stan Winston: Terminator, Alien's and Predator

Unlike the majority of today's monster makers, Stan Winston didn't grow up with any burning desire to transform himself or his friends into apes, visitors from outer space, the Frankenstein Monster, or hideously burned or mutilated accident victims. A graduate of the University of Virginia, Winston originally entertained plans of becoming an actor, moving west to Los Angeles the day he finished college: "I was a fine arts major. I painted, sketched and sculpted and I minored in drama. My interest in films was the creation and development of fantasy characters. It wasn't just what they looked like, it was who they *were*. I initially thought I was going to create characters as an actor. I had always been intrigued by actors in make-up — Charles Laughton as *The Hunchback of Notre Dame*, Spencer Tracy as *Dr.*

Opposite top: *Forty-one year-old Cicely Tyson as Miss Jane Pittman, a collaboration between Winston and Baker.*
Opposite bottom: *Stan Winston applying prosthetic pieces to Cicely Tyson.*
Left: *One of the colonists falls prey to a chestburster in* Aliens

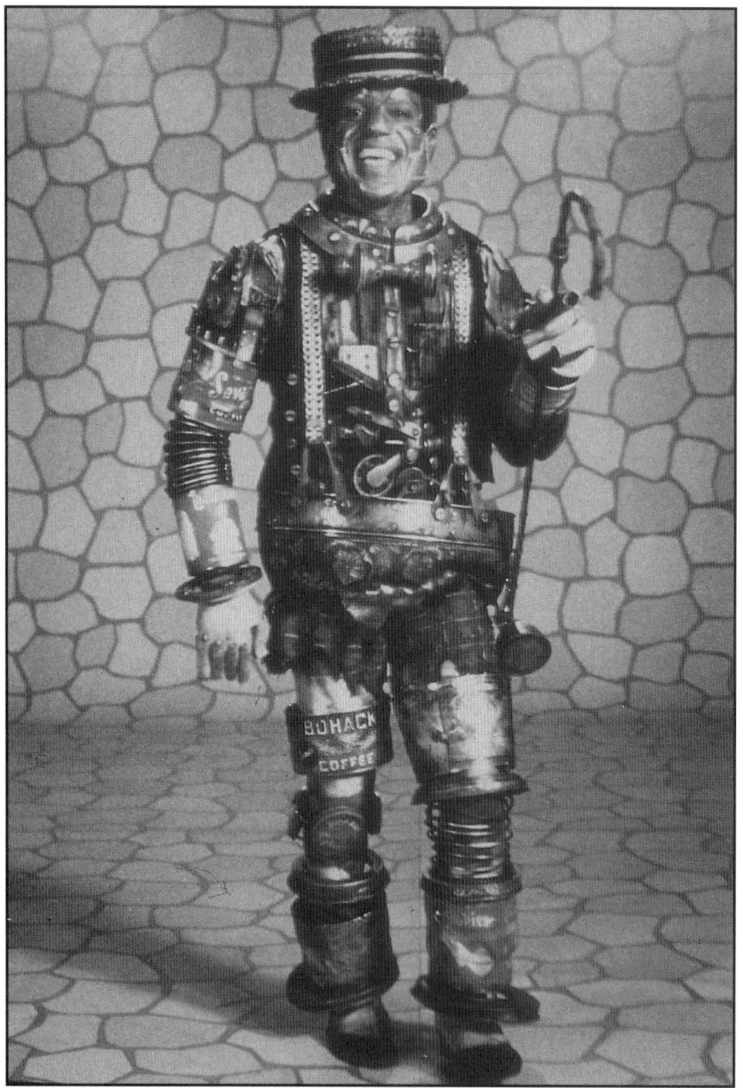

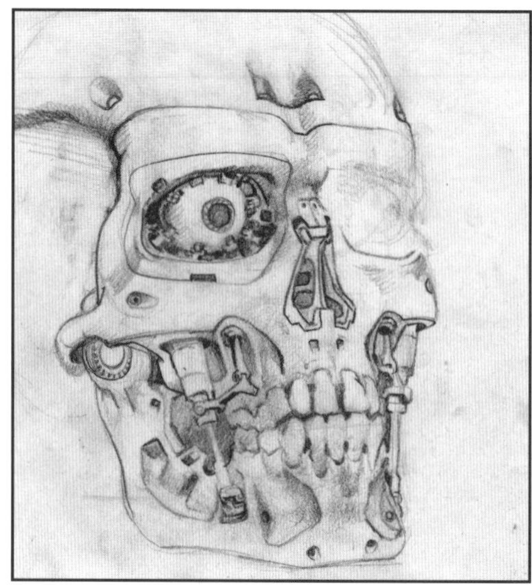

Jekyll and Mr. Hyde (1941). And whether they required a simple make-up or were extensive creatures, what was intriguing to me, and still is, was the creation of historic characters."

While waiting for his acting break, and eager to work in any area of the film industry, Winston enrolled on a make-up apprentice programme, one of only two students to be selected from more than 200 applicants. Placed under the tutelage of Robert Schiffer, then head of make-up at Walt Disney Productions, Winston began a 6,000-hour apprenticeship in 1969, before heading out on his own. His first job was the Emmy award-winning TV movie *Gargoyles*, where he designed and sculpted a number of background creatures as well as applying Bernie Casey's lead gargoyle make-up. Winston had pretty much begged for the job, which he saw as an ideal opportunity to show off his talent as a 'character' designer: "I went after *Gargoyles*, I *wanted* that movie, and I got to make monsters."

The following year Winston collaborated with Rick Baker on *The Autobiography of Miss Jane Pittman*, winning his second Emmy for Cicely Tyson's old-age make-up: "The best thing you can do is try to work with the most talented people. When I had the chance to work with Rick on *Jane Pittman*, I knew how good he was by virtue of the fact he had apprenticed, so to speak, with Dick Smith. Many people would look at me and say, 'Don't you feel you want to do it on your own?' But for me, that collaboration made my work stronger. I may not be the only author of the make-up, but I guarantee the final outcome was better because of our collaboration."

Between 1973 and 1979, Winston was nominated for a further half-dozen Emmys, including one for his work on Alex Haley's historical epic *Roots*, ageing Ben Vereen, Chuck Connors and Sandy Duncan among others.

"I have gone through a rather interesting and fun career that has stemmed from being typecast, just as an actor or a director gets typecast. And every time you try to break away, you become typecast in the next element. For *Gargoyles*, I helped to make-up Bernie Casey. Now, Bernie is black. I had done Cicely Tyson as a 110 year-old *black* slave. Then *Roots* comes along, and obviously it has old black people in it. So the person they go to is the guy who does old, black people. When I was doing *Roots*, Diana Ross came to me because she wanted to play three different ladies in black history — Ethel Waters, Bessie Smith and Josephine Baker — for a TV special. Naturally she is going to hire the guy who does all the black people. Then Diana starred in *The Wiz* (1978). She didn't have to wear any make-up, but all the rest of the characters did. It's a black *Wizard of Oz*. Now it was filmed in New York, which is Dick Smith's home town, but why wasn't Dick doing it? Because they want the *black* make-up artist. Diana Ross recommended me very highly for the show, and I'll never forget the look on their faces in the production office when I walked in — a *white, Jewish guy*. Everybody had expected me to be black."

In addition to designing all the prosthetic make-ups for *The Wiz*, which included Michael Jackson as the Scarecrow, Winston, in conjunction with the special effects department at Universal Studios, developed the film's army of flying monkeys. It was Winston's first foray into the world of mechanics and how they could be used to articulate faces. Later, when he had to

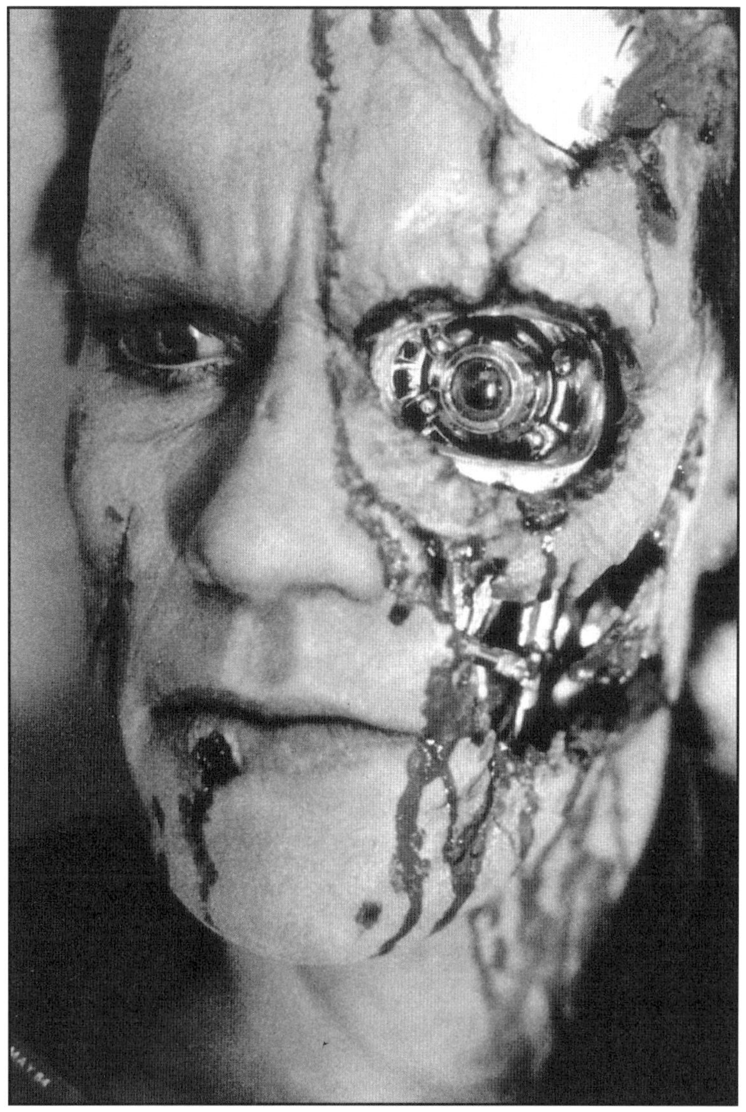

recreate Chewbacca and a family of Wookies for the *Star Wars TV Special*, Winston had the original Wookie head created by Stuart Freeborn for *Star Wars* sent over from England. Winston took it apart and used it as the basis for his designs. Refining his mechanical skills on *The Exterminator* (1980), where he devised a realistic decapitation, and *Dead and Buried* (1981), for which he created an articulated burn victim, Winston again found himself fortuitously typecast, when the producers of *Heartbeeps* were searching for someone to create a number of robotic make-ups for their film. "They had seen the Tin Man I had made for *The Wiz*," explains Winston. "It was a make-up that gave the illusion of Nipsey Russell having a metal face. In *Heartbeeps*, Bernadette Peters and Andy Kaufman play robotic characters, so naturally they're going to get the guy who does metallic make-ups. Now, that's not to say Rick Baker couldn't do it. But again it's typecasting." To

Opposite top left: *Nipsey Russell in Stan Winston's Tin Man make-up from* The Wiz.
Opposite top right: *Winston's sketch of the Terminator's skull.*
Opposite bottom left: *Director James Cameron's concept for the Terminator, a part he initially meant for Lance Henriksen.*
Above: *Winston's puppet head of the Terminator.*
Left: *Arnold Schwarzenegger as the Terminator with a fake arm built by Winston.*

Above left: *Winston details the endoskeleton body.* ***Above right:*** *Working on the skull of the Terminator.* ***Below left and right:*** *Rod and cable controlled puppets of the alien warriors were built by Winston and his crew for* Aliens.

transform Peters and Kaufman, Winston resurrected the long-discarded make-up technique of using a translucent gelatine instead of foam latex appliances to cover the actors' faces. The film secured Winston an Oscar nomination, though he was beaten to the award by Rick Baker for his work on *An American Werewolf in London*. Winston's next task was more straightforward, creating a robotic face for the lead singer of rock band Styx to wear in their video *Mr. Roboto*: "They needed a robot and I was the guy who did robotic make-ups. So I wonder where James Cameron's going to go when its time to do *The Terminator* (1984)? Also, I was into puppetry — I had done the dog thing for *The Thing*. So it was natural for Cameron to call me. In fact, I was recommended to him by Dick Smith."

Produced for a modest $6,500,000, writer-director James Cameron's *The Terminator* event-

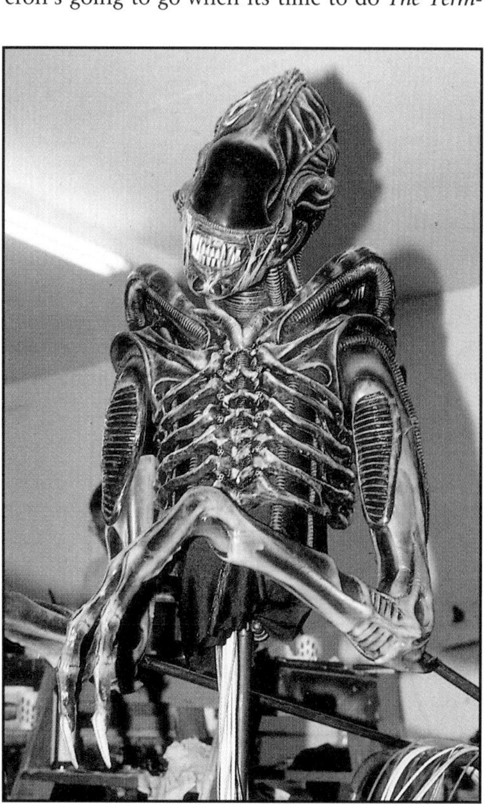

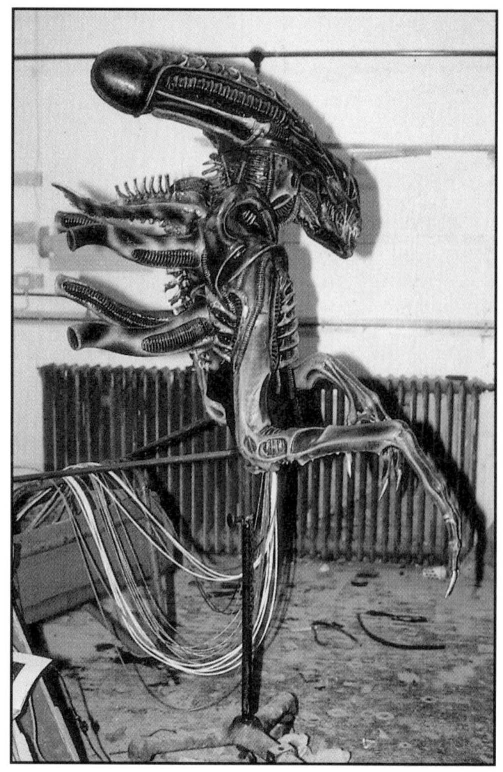

ually took over $40,000,000 at the box office and made stars of its director, make-up artist and lead (Arnold Schwarzenegger). It also forged a partnership between Cameron and Winston that would later come to remarkable fruition with their work on *Aliens* (1986) and *Terminator 2: Judgment Day* (1991). Cameron, a former special effects supervisor and production designer for New World Pictures who up until then had directed only the instantly forgettable *Piranha II Flying Killers* (1981), had an idea for a script based around the image of a human robot which walks out of a fire shorn of its synthetic skin, revealing itself to be a metallic endoskeleton. Working backwards from this basic concept, Cameron came up with the story of an indestructible human cyborg from the future (a role that would eventually be played by Schwarzenegger) returning to the present to kill the mother (Linda Hamilton) of his as yet unborn enemy.

An excellent artist in his own right, Cameron had sketched out a rough design for the Terminator in its metallic form prior to contacting Winston. "I saw the Terminator before I saw the script," Winston recalls. "Jim showed me a painting he had done of the endoskeleton, and it was like, 'Wow, that'll be a challenge.'" Although it was Cameron's intention to give Winston full creative freedom in designing the robot, he was so enamoured with Cameron's concept that he had no desire to alter it: "Jim happens to be an incredible artist, which was great for me because most of the time my biggest problem is working with directors who don't have an artistic concept. In this case there was already one that was brilliant, and I didn't want to change it."

Top: *The Queen Alien's tongue mechanism being tested.*
Above: *A warrior suit is put through its paces.*
Left: *The Queen Alien.*

With his crew of make-up and mechanical effects technicians, Winston built the endoskeleton, as well as several mechanised replicas of Schwarzenegger's head and a number of prosthetic facial appliances that would be worn by the actor to simulate the Terminator's varying states of disrepair. From a resculpted lifecast of Schwarzenegger, Winston constructed three puppet heads. The first of these is seen when the Terminator repairs to a sleazy motel room to effect makeshift ocular surgery to injuries sustained in his unsuccessful attack on Hamilton at the Tech Noir nightclub, and inserts a scalpel into his eye. The second shows the result of his handiwork, uncovering the metallic skull beneath the

HEARTBEEPS GELATINE MAKE-UP

Above: *Stan Winston sculpts the appliances for* Heartbeeps. ***Below left and right:*** *Bernadette Peters as Aqua and the late Andy Kaufman as the robot Vaz.*

Stan Winston's make-ups for Andy Kaufman and Bernadette Peters robot characters Val and Aqua were not made from the standard foam latex, but from gelatine, the basic ingredient of jelly.

Winston first took lifecasts of Kaufman and Peters, then sculpted back in any detail that had been lost during the casting process. Working from these corrected lifecasts, Winston then sculpted the seven different pieces that would make up Peters' character's face, while fellow artist Mike McCracken sculpted Kaufman's under Winston's supervision. The seven pieces were moulded in the usual way, but Winston decided that foam latex would not provide the translucent effect he'd sought and so turned to gelatine.

Gelatine had been used frequently before the development of foam, and to a lesser extent, afterwards, notably in *The Good Earth* (1937), turning American actors into convincing Orientals, and on *Caesar and Cleopatra* (1945), providing the bald head for Claude Rains. Gelatine has some advantages over foam latex, as when it is melted and poured into moulds it takes a shorter time to set, while foam requires a long baking time. Also, it moves well on the face, and doesn't wrinkle and its edges can be literally dissolved to hide them. But though gelatine has been in regular use, it has two major disadvantages. Firstly, it is a heavy material and so rarely employed for anything other than small appliances. Secondly, and more importantly, it is prone to melting, or, to be more precise, dissolving due to the sweat of the actor, which acts like acid and causes it to break down into a mush. To combat this, Winston and his crew added chemicals to the formula; a method that was only partially successful, as two complete sets of replacement pieces were needed every day since the thin sections would disintegrate halfway through the shoot.

Finally, Winston chose to colour his make-ups with a range of metallic paints mixed with pearlescent pigment, a mixture of bronze, silver and gold used to create a unique make-up. ■

Terminator's synthetic skin, while the third was built for use after the Terminator has been dragged beneath the petrol tanker during the film's finale, resulting in the majority of its flesh being torn away.

Winston also fabricated a prosthetic arm and hand for use in the motel sequence, allowing Schwarzenegger's cyborg to peel back its skin and reveal its mechanical workings. Ironically, Winston did a matching make-up of the third puppet head on Schwarzenegger which Cameron preferred, and so consequently used the puppet only for extreme close-ups. For the make-up, Winston placed thin vacuum-metalised plastic pieces directly onto Schwarzenegger's face, on top of which he glued foam rubber appliances sculpted to match the look of the puppet head with its skin torn away. Then mechanics were painted in relief form onto the metalised plate, while for the red glowing eye effect a tiny lightbulb and thin red lens were laid on top of Schwarzenegger's eye and connected to a wire that ran over his ear and down his back.

The film's most striking image is the very one that fuelled Cameron's imagination in the first place — that of the endoskeleton rising phoenix-like from the wreckage of an exploding petrol tanker. While the majority of the shots featuring the full length walking endoskeleton were filmed using a two foot tall stop-motion model, a full-

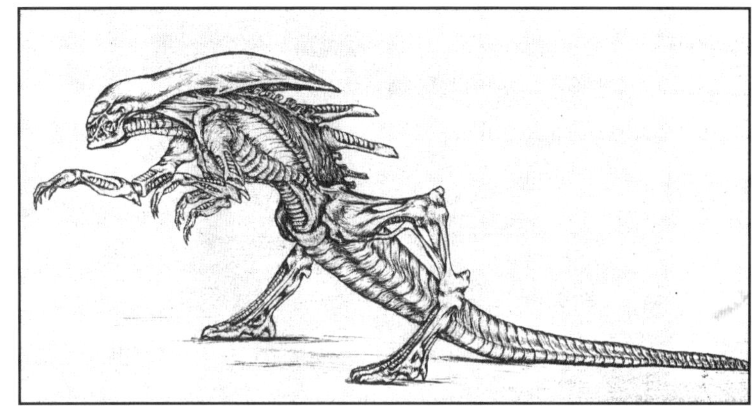

Top: *Winston's sketch of an alternative design for the Queen Alien.* ***Above:*** *The Queen Alien in her nest.* ***Left:*** *Cameron's painting of the climactic confrontation between the Queen Alien and Sigourney Weaver wearing a power loader.*

Opposite: *Character designer Stan Winston with his creations.* ***Right:*** *Winston directs a garbage bag and foam mock-up of the Queen Alien.* ***Below left:*** *Winston crew member Shane Mahan details a face hugger for the dissection scene in* Aliens. ***Below right:*** *John Rosengrant painting the Queen Alien's body.*

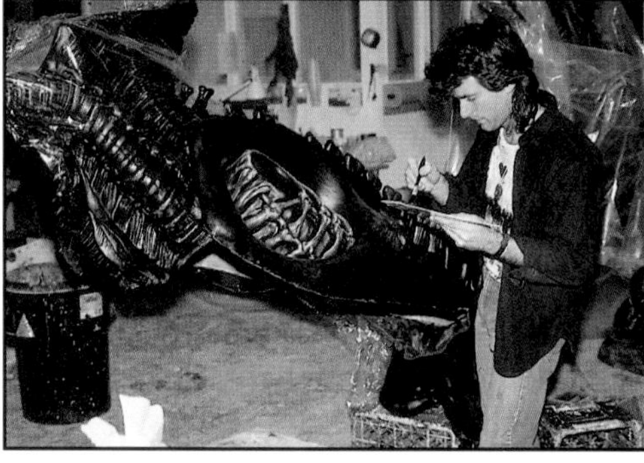

size version was also employed. Sculpted in clay, then cast in chromed epoxy with steel reinforcement, it took Winston and his crew six months to create. "Jim's concept of the robot was that it be organic but look like a machine," explains Winston, who felt it was important to retain Schwarzenegger's size and form in building the endoskeleton. "Not only is the robot the same height as Arnold, but all of its proportions are scaled down and matched to fit his. The robot is anatomically correct and could literally fit inside Arnold's body.

"But did *I* create the Terminator? Absolutely not. I was a *part* of creating the Terminator. I may have been responsible for the physical representation in the final analysis of the Terminator robot, and of Arnold as the Terminator, but it came from Jim Cameron's mind, it was an original piece of artwork from Jim Cameron. And obviously many people went to see the film because of Arnold Schwarzenegger. So there are all of these pieces in the mix that are part of you becoming a success."

When James Cameron took up the challenge of directing a sequel to Ridley Scott's brilliantly realised sci-fi shocker *Alien*, he turned inevitably to his *Terminator* collaborator Stan Winston to provide the hordes of acid-blooded xenomorphs that do battle with Sigourney Weaver and a troop of gung-ho colonial marines. It won Winston his first Oscar for make-up effects: "*Aliens* was an incredible challenge for a number of reasons. Number one: working with Cameron is a challenge in itself. Since *The Terminator* we had been very close friends, but he is not an easy person to please; he is very *specific*. Number two: *Alien* is one of my favourite horror films of all time. It was a *perfect* film. Everything about it was memorable. It was the horror film of the decade. So how can you do anything but lose trying to do a sequel to a classic film? Well, the answer to how it was going to be different and/or better than *Alien* was — Jim Cameron. I knew he was going to do something special. If it had been any other director there is a good chance I would not have done the film."

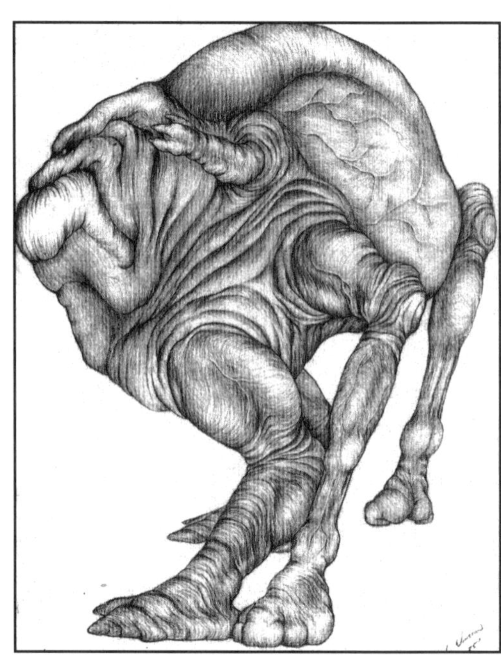

***Right:** Winston's sketch for the* Invaders from Mars *drones.* ***Below:** The supreme intelligence as drawn by Winston for* Invaders from Mars. ***Bottom:** The internal harness for the Martian drones.*

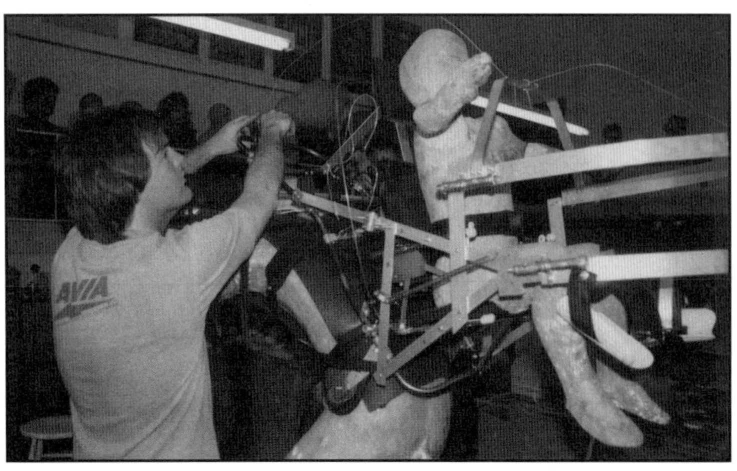

Cameron's script, as the title suggests, called not just for one alien, but for a veritable army. Working from Swiss surrealist H.R. Giger's highly recognisable alien design for Scott's film, Winston and his forty man crew produced up to a dozen alien warriors as well as the fourteen foot high Alien Queen with which Weaver does battle at the film's climax. "What we had to do was be honest to the first film, to recreate the original characters so the audience did not feel cheated," explains Winston, who had started his own studio after the success of *The Terminator*, "and also give them the ability to perform more, so you could extend their character. In the first film, when you saw a face-hugger it was just something on a person's face which was then thrown away. In *Aliens* we had face-huggers running all over the place, having to act. We stayed legitimate to the original concept, but finessed the sculpture a little bit. That's how we improved on the original. Each of our characters did more. We developed the suits for the alien warriors so that the actors wearing them could perform more action than in the original."

Winston achieved this greater freedom of movement for his alien warriors by eliminating Rambaldi's heavy latex suit, using instead foam rubber appliances attached to a lightweight black bodysuit that the actors would wear: "Probably the only imperfect thing about *Alien* was at the end, seeing it come out of the spaceship and realising it was a man in a suit. I liked it better when we didn't see it. We stayed with Giger's concept, but — and these were ideas of Jim's — by doing reverse shots, changing the speed of the film, we gave them the ability to act like insects. They were shot in such a way that you never really saw the man in a suit. We *never* allowed you to see that. Giger's designs were absolutely incredible, but it was a challenge to be able to finesse the artwork a little bit with our technology. It would have probably been frustrating, however, had we not had the Queen Alien to play about with. That was our *pièce de résistance*."

The Queen Alien was based on a design of Cameron's, which Winston was so taken with that, as with *The Terminator* endoskeleton, he constructed to the director's exact specifications. The Queen utilised a concept similar to the one Winston had used for the Martian drones in Tobe Hooper's 1986 remake of the William Cameron Menzies classic *Invaders from Mars* (1953): "I had shown Jim the concept of the reverse 'body' with the little person strapped on to another guy's back I had come up with on *Invaders*. Whether that triggered his imagination to having two people inside the Queen, I couldn't really say. But I was working on that when Jim came to me. His concept was, 'Let's put two people inside a suit and fly them on a crane to make the Queen work.' In one breath I said, 'You're out of your mind.' In the next, I said, 'Yeah, it'll probably work,' because Jim wouldn't have thought of it otherwise, because that's who he is.

"We made a rough mock-up of the Queen using black foam core and plastic garbage bags, and suspended our stuntmen inside it. For the big arms we used ski pole extensions and attached them to some creature hands I had developed for

Above left: *A conceptual sketch of the* Leviathan *creature.*
Above right: *Early sketches for the Predator.*
Left: *Stan Winston Studios also designed the Predator's armour.*

Right: *Sculpting the Predator's foot.* **Far right:** *Airbrushing the suit.* **Below:** *Testing the Predator's suit.*

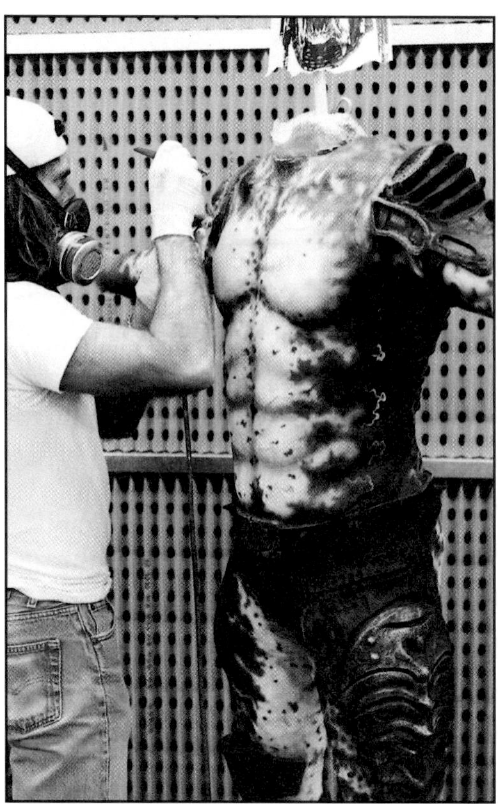

another project. We set this thing up in our parking lot to see if it was going to work — and it did. There was a lot of fine tuning to be done, but the basic concept was good."

On set, it took fourteen puppeteers to operate the Queen, in addition to the two lucky enough to be inside it.

"Somebody once described it as an anorexic dinosaur," remembers Cameron, "which I suppose is inevitable, but it's not what I had in mind. In fact, I wanted specifically not to suggest a dinosaur concept. For me, the Queen is a blend of what Giger does with what I wanted to do, which was to create something that was big and powerful and terrifying and fast and very female. Hideous and beautiful at the same time, like a black widow spider."

After the myriad hordes of *Aliens*, creating the single intergalactic hunter that picks off a group of mercenaries led by Arnold Schwarzenegger in John McTiernan's *Predator* (1987) must have seemed like a walk in the park for Winston. Brought in by producer Joel Silver on *Terminator* star Schwarzenegger's recommendation when the original creature designed by Boss Films was deemed impracticable for use on the jungle location in Palenque, Mexico, Winston ultimately went for a much simpler approach than that adopted by Boss. His concept for the Predator was a man (the late Kevin Peter Hall) wearing a foam latex suit and a mechanical mask — basing its design on a drawing of a dreadlocked Conan-like warrior given him by the film's producers.

"I remember saying to John McTiernan that for it to work, it has to be a *character*. The audience *has* to relate to it, it has to have a history. I hate to give Jim (*Cameron*) too much credit, but when I was drawing the basic concept of the Predator he mentioned something to me about insects and mandibles. And being the 'thief' of ideas that I am, I'm drawing it, going, 'Oh, *that's* interesting.' So even the Predator has a little bit of Jim Cameron in him."

A massive box success, *Predator* both spawned a sequel and earned Winston his third Oscar nomination: "The Terminator, the Queen Alien, the Predator will all be around long after I'm

Left: *The title creature from* Vengeance the Demon.
Below: *Fitting* Edward *with his scissorhands.*

dead. People will remember my work, and it's a wonderful feeling. They are all historic characters and I am fortunate that I have been part of their creation. I say part, because it is very important for us all to realise that what we do is an *added* element. It takes the written word, a good screenplay, strong direction. If it is make-up, or a prosthetic or a mechanical prosthetic on an actor, as was the Predator, as was Rick Baker's Harry, then it's the performance.

"If I am doing a make-up on an actor, the best thing I can possibly do is assist that actor in finding the character. We are assisting by giving him a physicality. If we are doing a character that is completely animatronic, then Stan Winston becomes the actor via all the people who work with me; so Cameron is talking to me as though I'm the actor. 'What is the Alien Queen going to do right now? How are we going to create a dynamic performance out of her?' Is Jim talking to

In 1988, Winston was approached by the producers of *Vengeance the Demon* to create the film's seven foot tall gangly demon summoned by a vengeful Lance Henriksen after his son is killed by a group of tourists. He agreed, providing he could direct the film. Well acquainted with the fantasy/horror genre, and having acted as second-unit director on both *The Terminator* and *Aliens*, Winston revealed himself to be a more than competent director, delegating the entire design and construction of the film's title creature to his studio.

Two years later, Winston was contacted by Tim Burton to work on the first of two films that would satisfy his desire for creating memorable characters: "*Edward Scissorhands* (1990) was a real stretch. There was really nothing in my career that said this is why Tim should go to Stan, other than that I had a reputation of having a wide range, and anything we did, we did well. It was wonderful for me to have to dispense with reality and bring about the vision of Tim Burton, who has a very theatrical and cartoon aspect of mind. I loved it because I am so reality grounded, and I had to take those straps off and free up, and become a messenger of Burton's vision. As a result, I was much more into Tim's mind by the time I designed Danny De Vito as the Penguin in *Batman Returns* (1992).

"The first thing I said when I read about this guy who has scissors for hands was that it made no sense. Tim's cartoon sketch for Edward made no sense. Edward Scissorhands, finished in the film, makes no sense. So you can either look at it

Above: *Johnny Depp in the title role of Tim Burton's* Edward Scissorhands. **Right:** *Winston with the star of his second directorial outing,* A Gnome Called Gnorm. **Far right:** *The Penguin's make-up from* Batman Returns.

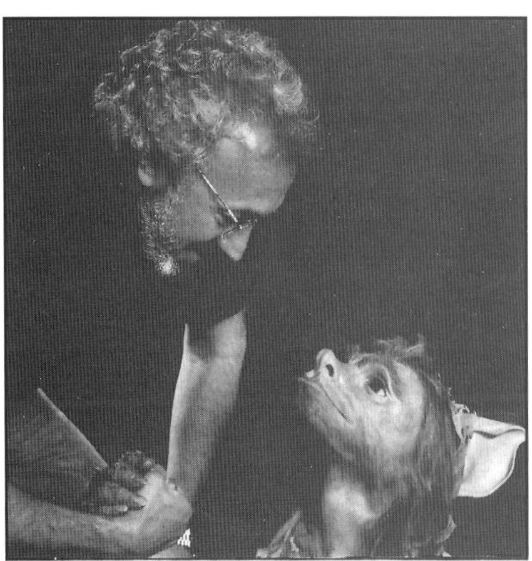

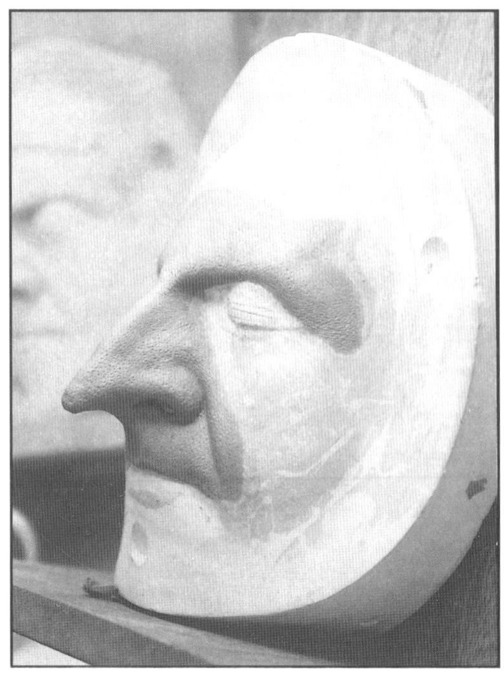

the Queen or is he talking to me? He's talking to me, and then I'm talking to all the puppeteers, so, in essence, I become the actor, which is what I set out to do when I came to Hollywood."

and go, 'This is stupid, I want to have no part of it.' Or you can go, 'Well, he's got scars on his face, he's got scissors for hands. Now, let's see how we can make those scissors interesting and make *you* believe they're real.' Tim and I spent a great deal of time sketching, coming up with an interesting concept that looked *neat*. By taking that absurd concept and making all of the elements as real as I possibly could, it *almost* made sense.

"In some ways it's very difficult to deal with Tim because he says, 'It's sort of like a thing, and it has hair and there's scissors and a thing...' and you're going, 'I *think* I know what he's saying.' It's not the words, it's getting into that person's head. It's very important for me to create a character that fits seamlessly into a storyline, that fits into a particular look, a production design. If I had put a totally realistic character in the place of Edward it would not have worked: that wasn't the movie, it's not Tim Burton. When you look at Danny De Vito as the Penguin, I designed him — Tim usually does a cartoon rendering of the basic broad concept — but it's my vision of how his face should look for Tim Burton.

"If you look at Edward or the Penguin, you see a signature — you see Tim Burton more than you see Stan Winston. If that character fits, I have done my job successfully. You look at *The Terminator*, *Aliens*, you are looking at a Jim Cameron film, you are looking at Jim Cameron creations. They are not Stan Winston creations. Even if I draw or sculpt them, in the final analysis, it's the director." ■

***Top:** Detailing the Penguin's make-up over a cast of Danny De Vito.*
***Above:** A penguin suit for* Batman Returns.
***Left:** A few of the Penguin's loyal henchman puppets.*

Chapter Eleven

Life's abyss and then you dive

Steve Johnson: The Abyss and later work

To create the race of pacifist aliens for his underwater spectacular *The Abyss* (1989), director James Cameron turned once again to Stan Winston who, because of other commitments, had to pass on the assignment. After considering the alternatives, Cameron chose Steve Johnson, who since leaving Boss in 1986 had set up his own company, XFX Inc, and provided effects for a number of lower-budgeted features, including *A Nightmare on Elm Street IV: The Dream Master* (1988), *Dead Heat* (1988) and *Night of the Demons* (1987). Johnson was given just four months to create eight transparent alien puppets that would work underwater, a task made even harder because none of the conceptual artists who had been brought on board before him to design the

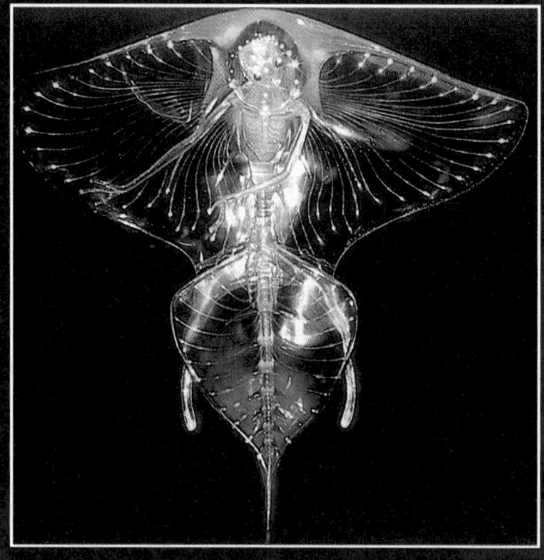

Opposite top: *An underwater alien from James Cameron's* The Abyss, *one of Johnson's most difficult assignments.*
Opposite bottom: *An early design for* The Abyss *aliens by Steve Johnson and James Kagel.*
Left: *Hell cop make-up from* Highway to Hell.

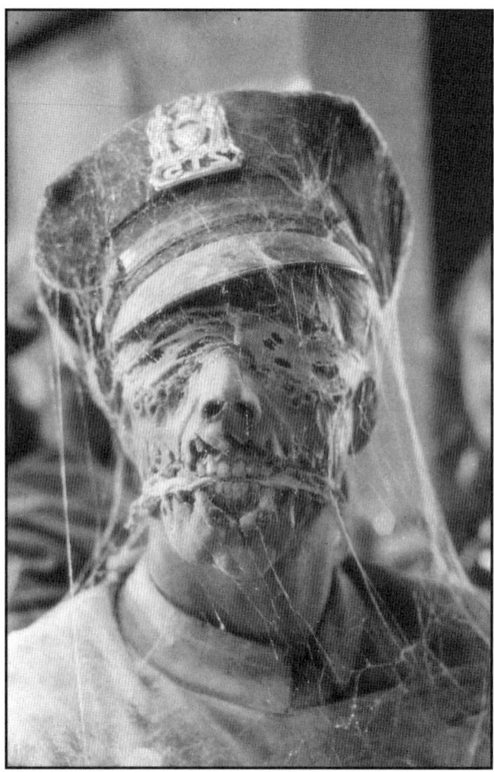

creatures could successfully capture the vision Cameron had in his head. "Jim Cameron asked me to make the most beautiful alien ever," recalls Johnson, "one that would illuminate itself, change colour, be glass-clear *and* work underwater. I didn't know if I could do it or not. I just thought, 'What a great opportunity, how can I turn this down?'"

But with no approved design to speak of, and a deadline to keep, Johnson began toying with a concept of his own, one that was a cross between a man and a manta ray. The design met with everybody's approval — except the director's. So while further revisions were called for, Johnson began the arduous task of finding a material that would adhere to Cameron's specifications: "*The Abyss* was the only job I've ever taken where there were times I lost sleep. I thought, 'My God, this is crazy, I'm going to ruin my career with this, I don't think it can be done.' Making something work underwater is immediately the hardest thing you can be asked to do. Making something transparent — how many times has that been done? Making something glow and change colour — *not* easy. Put them all together — it's crazy. If we found materials that would work underwater and would be clear, we couldn't make them glow. If we found materials that would glow and would work underwater, they wouldn't be clear. It was a real nightmare. But we figured it out."

Above left: *Johnson details one of the transparent* Abyss *aliens.* ***Above right:*** *Zombie cop from* Highway to Hell. ***Below:*** *Rachel demon from* Highway to Hell.

Johnson's solution was to make a series of puppets using a combination of transparent plastic and clear flexible urethanes, illuminated by fibre optics and manipulated by both rods and wires: "I've never worked with a director who was as specific as Cameron. There are good and bad sides to that. When all was said and done, and I finished the show several grey hairs later, I looked at it, and the whole time I almost felt like I was a puppet, because I was directed so specifically in how it should look. I never had an idea as to how we would pull it off — that was the hard part."

Johnson has nothing but praise for the director, however: "Cameron pushes and pushes and pushes — that's the good thing about him. He will always push the envelope and make you do what you think is impossible. No-one else would have gotten that out of someone. I really respected the hell out of him. Since he does have enough of a background in special effects, he wasn't like some goofball director that's never done a movie. He had enough of a handle to

know it *was* possible. So that gave me faith, to think that we could eventually figure it out. But it was tough, it was definitely the toughest thing I've ever done."

Following *The Abyss,* Johnson worked on the little-seen *Highway to Hell* (1990), in which a pair of love-struck teenagers take a wrong turn while driving to Las Vegas and wind up in Hell: "The script was really good, but I think it needed about three times the budget to pull it off. It was very much a character design exercise, because there were several things that really required a lot of thought. In the script, the Hell Cop was described as 'a lizard-like zombie'. And what two things have been the most overdone in this business? Lizard-men and zombies. But there was some mention about the texture of his face, so I thought, 'What if it was something subtle, something that could be mistaken for bad skin, but on closer inspection, you'd see there were words covering his face. There are only a few shots where you can read them, and that kinda makes it even neater." If you could read them, you'd see that Johnson inserted a number of in-jokes for his own amusement, including 'Savini Rules' and 'SJ + LQ', the latter an amorous reference to his B-movie actress-wife Linnea Quigley.

Johnson also created the horned-demon Rachel, an exploding head effect, a pair of *hand*-cuffs that are literally disembodied hands, a series of Andy Warhol masks, and a devil make-up for Patrick Bergin: "As the make-up started going on, and Patrick saw how it worked and moved, he got so excited. He was a fairly quiet guy throughout the shoot, and yet he was so extrovert that day it was incredible. He went into the character, and really appreciated the make-up and what it did for him and his character. And I got chills watching him on the set — it was just fantastic seeing that make-up come to life."

With *The Temp* (1993), a psycho bitch from hell movie starring Lara Flynn Boyle as Timothy Hutton's rather unhinged secretary, Johnson renewed his association with *Fright Night* director Tom Holland: "I had several hundred thousand dollars to do a lot of effects. There were dream scenes, bugs pouring out of Tim Hutton's chest, Lara Flynn Boyle and Tim and getting caught up in all kinds of machinery. We made full mechanical puppets that were set on fire, she got sliced and slashed, he got beaten up, there were dead

Left: *Stuey monster from* Freaked.
Below: *Mechanical arm rig for the paper shredder sequence from* The Temp. *One of many of Johnson's effects that were cut from the final film.*
Bottom: *Megan Ward with fake head and arm of actor Michael Stoyanov — the Siamese twins from* Freaked.

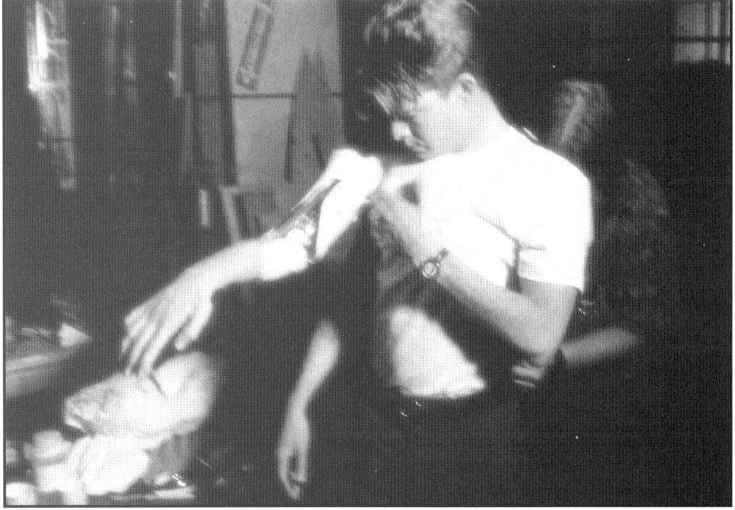

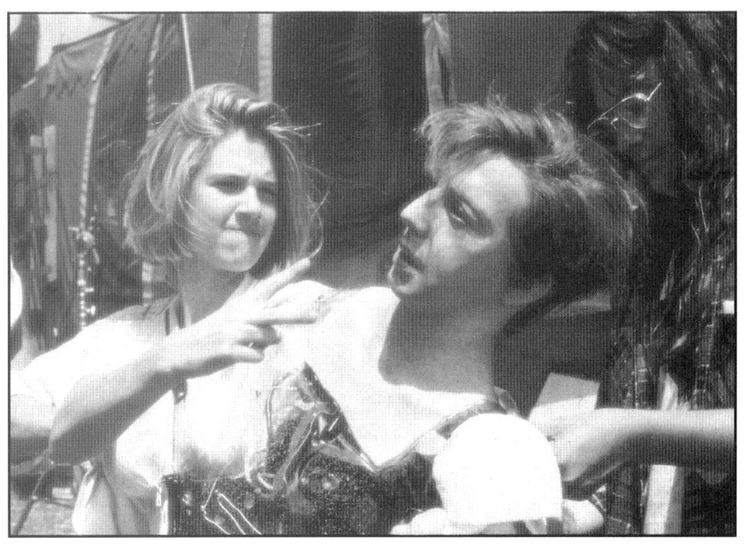

***Above:** Applying Alex Winter's make-up for* Freaked.
***Right:** For* Freaked, *Johnson designed director Alex Winter's Rick.*
***Below right:** A mummy, created by Johnson for a beer commercial.*

make-ups on people. It was a lot of work. And they cut *everything*. They pulled them out, because in the end they didn't want it to be a horror film.

"We also did this beautiful prosthetic make-up on a guy who hangs himself, a bloated dead guy, with his eyes all bugged out. But we actually re-shot that just with a painted make-up because it was *too* horrifying. The *only* thing that was left in the film is a guy who dies by wasp stings. We did a gelatine appliance to give the impression that his face is all puffed up and swollen."

Fortunately for Johnson, his work in Gus Van Sant's adaptation of Tom Robbins' novel *Even Cowgirls Get the Blues* (1993) played an all-too important role to be cut, since his crew designed and constructed sixty pairs of over-sized thumbs worn by lead Uma Thurman.

In comparison to *Cowgirls'* naturalistic tone, Alex Winter and Tom Stern's *Freaked* (1993) allowed Johnson's imagination to run riot, and he created a number of wacky, surreal and cartoon-like effects for the distinctly odd film: "We did some incredibly cool stuff on *Freaked*. Actually, *everything* we did is really cool in that movie." Johnson's favourite, however, is the half-normal, half-cartoon face worn by star Winter: "When they first came to me, they had this idea to give him a split face. So I went through all number of different ideas, and I kept saying to myself, 'He's gotta go through this make-up for more than thirty days, we need to keep it to something that's fairly simple.' So I came up with an idea that I had played around with on *Fright Night*." Since Winter was also the film's co-director, the make-up needed to be doubly durable. "He slept in the make-up a lot," remembers Johnson. "It was really bizarre, I've never known that to happen. Several times he slept in it two nights in a row; once he slept in it three nights in a row. So we got almost a full week's shoot with one application. It was unbelievable. And it looks great. It's flawless. We would then just spend an hour the next day touching it up and repainting. Alex was a real trouper about it."

Johnson's crew also created a pair of eight foot tall, bug-eyed monsters and male-female Siamese twins, the latter of which he is particularly proud: "How many times have you seen a movie where you have something with two heads that's absolutely laughable, where they stick an actor's head up behind another guy's shoulder or put a stupid-looking puppet on somebody. What we did to pull it off was use every trick we possibly could, and I think it's the best two-headed thing

ever done, actually. There's something different in every shot." Indeed, Johnson made full use of computers, fully articulated, remote-controlled puppets and every possible combination of real-person/false arm/head/leg/body to achieve the effect. Johnson's creative approach illustrates an ingenuity honed by his time working on low-budget films: "If you have an incredible amount of money, a lot of times that ties your hands, psychologically. You will think, 'Okay, I'll do it by starting at step one and ending at step ten.' And if it takes a lot of money and time, that's the way to do it. But if you have a limitation somewhere, if you have ten dollars to do an effect, you have to be incredibly creative, and I think a lot of times you will come up with a better alternative because it forces you to think sideways instead of straight ahead.

"For instance, on *Dead Heat*, one of my favourite effects in the movie is where Lindsay Frost deteriorates. For the first shot where her face starts to sag, all I did was glue some very, very thin but strong fabric to her face at several points and attach very thin fishing line to it, and then

Above left: *A zombie for* Dead Heat.
Above right: *Anne Parillaud wearing Johnson-designed colour-changing contact lenses from John Landis'* Innocent Blood.
Below left: *Bruce Payne in vampire make-up from* Howling VI: The Freaks.
Below right: *Three-faced zombie from* Dead Heat.

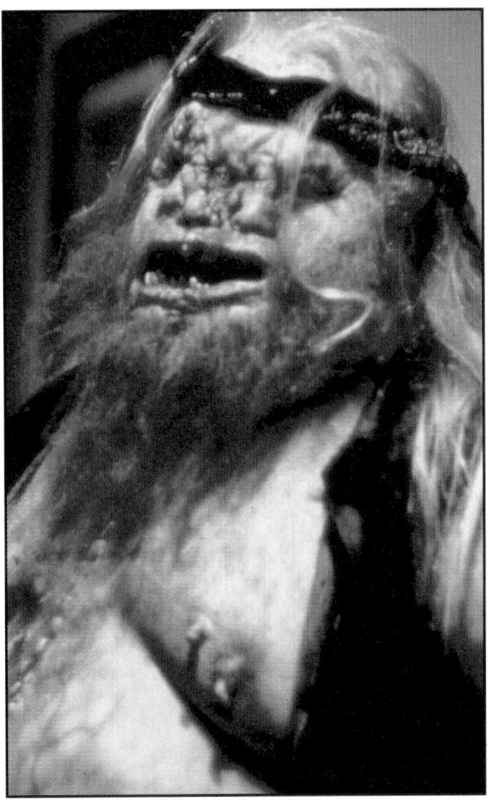

Right: Uma Thurman in Johnson's mechanical make-up thumbs. **Below:** An animatronic stegosaurus created by Johnson for a Japanese amusement park.

EVEN COWGIRLS GET THE BLUES

For writer-director Gus Van Sant's adaptation of Tom Robbins' cult novel *Even Cowgirls Get the Blues*, Steve Johnson was called upon to extend the thumbs of lead actress Uma Thurman to twice their normal size. "We had to mechanically extend Uma's thumbs," Johnson reveals. "And since she wears them every single day and has to ride horses, has to eat, has to do everything with these things, even behind the scenes, she has to go to the bathroom with these things on, they had to be practical, they had to work."

The solution was to create a self-contained mechanism within the fake digits that worked off the pivot of Thurman's own thumb. So when her thumb moved, it operated the additional extended joint: "There was no way we were going to be able to get away with any kind of remote control device — there just wasn't the room. We had something under the skin, and we had something like an inch-and-a-half by maybe three-eighths of an inch in circumference to work with."

Another major consideration was the sheer size of the job. Since Thurman was the star of the film, the thumbs were required on set virtually every day, meaning Johnson and his crew had to turn out in excess of sixty pairs of outsize thumbs and keep the quality perfect throughout: "So not only did we have to figure out the mechanism, we had to figure out ways to get that many appliances made that quickly. We had something like eight or nine weeks to prepare for it, so that was challenging enough in itself."

Additionally, Johnson had to make a series of progressive thumbs for the girls who were playing Thurman's character as she grows up, scaling down the mechanism to fit their tiny hands: "The six year-old thumb was really a bitch, because it was so tiny: it was the size of half your pinkie. It was a little watch mechanism basically." ■

pull her face down. And it just looked incredible. If you built a dummy it would cost $30,000 and wouldn't look half as good. And here it was, basically for free, in ten minutes."

Another example of Johnson's creativity can be seen in John Landis' *Innocent Blood* (1992) in which Gallic vampire Anne Parillaud sinks her teeth into Pittsburgh mobster Robert Loggia and his hoods: "John wanted to show something very special for the vampire's eyes. So we came up with a way to make contact lenses from a material that reflects a thousand per cent of light you shine on it. So whatever colour gel you put in front of the light the eyes will then change to that colour. So we could make them glow, and change colour in every shot, just by changing the gel." And in keeping with vampiric tradition, director Landis also had Johnson devise a disintegration effect. He created a mechanical puppet head of the unfortunate Don Rickles, which when pumped with a combination of sulphuric and nitric acid, resulted in a chemical reaction that would cause it to burn without flames: "It was amazing, these charred patterns crawled all over the face and then big chunks of flesh fell off."

Like so many of his contemporaries, running his own effects company has meant that Johnson has had to delegate much of the hands-on work to his crew, finding that the design process is now one of the few areas to which he can really devote any time: "It's also the one place where you can really, really have fun. I can't have my hands on the stuff any more, I can't go out there and sculpt and be satisfied because the phone is *always* ringing. The only time I can really get any work done with my own hands is late at night after people leave.

"So I had to find something else I could really get personally satisfied by, and that is the conceptualisation process, because there you're completely free — there are no limits, it doesn't cost any money to think up ideas. There's nothing that can go wrong in your head while you're thinking about it. The first time I had a chance to really try this out was on *Ghostbusters*. To come up with some really good ideas, I just climb way back up into the space in my head, and twist ideas around — almost look at them as if they were a computer graphics model. Twist these ideas and concepts around, see them from beginning to end, try to compare them to other things I've seen, look at them upside down, sideways, inside out, and just really, really spend a lot of time, making it real top-heavy in the thought process, before you ever get started. You can't lose that way. Also, it's real pure — it's just you and your head. Once it comes out of your head, it's a job — and you've got to do it." ■

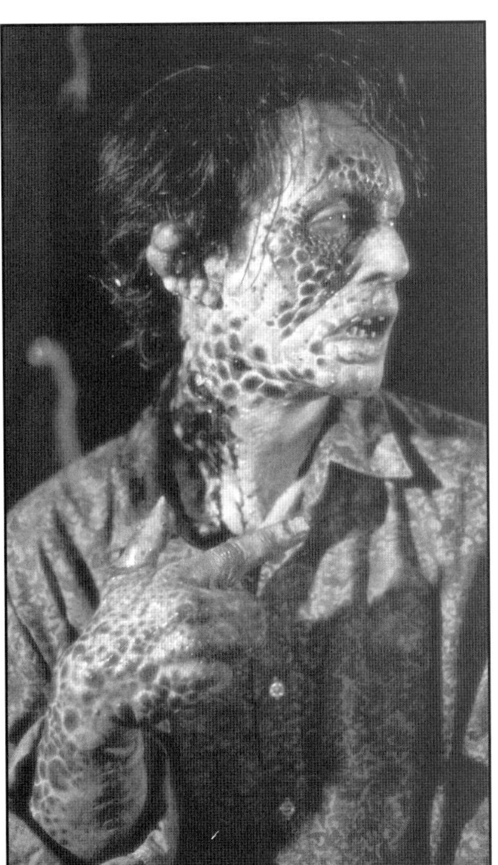

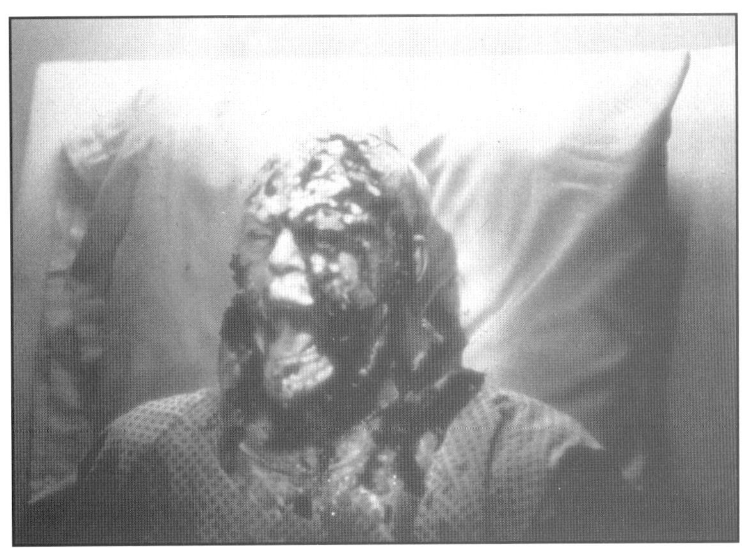

Above: *Alien from* Suburban Commando.
Below left: *Alligator boy make-up from* Howling VI: The Freaks.
Below right: *Steve Johnson's deteriorating Don Rickles puppet. The head was pumped with acid to create this effect in* Innocent Blood.

Chapter Twelve

Apes, gremlins and dinosaurs

Rick Baker's work since Harry and the Hendersons

Baker won his second Academy Award in 1988 for what is arguably his most expressive and endearing creation, the bigfoot Harry who befriends a holidaying family in William Dear's *Harry and the Hendersons*. Played with remarkable empathy by *Predator*'s Kevin Peter Hall, Harry, although not strictly an ape, is clearly of simian descent and his expressive facial movements are a reflection of Baker's study and love of apes. Credit must also go to Hall, who gives a touching performance despite having his whole face, save his eyes, obscured by a mechanical mask. "Harry was a character with soul, and that *had* to show on his face," says Baker. "I see Harry as the evolution of make-up."

Later that year, Baker finally achieved his life's ambition, creating the most realistic depiction of simians ever committed to celluloid for Michael Apted's *Gorillas in the Mist*. Based on the true story of Diane Fossey and her life-long obsession with the African mountain gorilla, Apted's film was the perfect outlet for Baker's passion for apes: "When they talked to me about *Gorillas*, I said, 'Listen, I can make an ape suit better than anybody, I've lived my life to make the ultimate ape suit.' And finally, with this film, I was able to make the suit I had *always* wanted to make." Indeed, such was his involvement and interest in the subject matter that he was also credited as the film's associate producer.

Two years later, Baker took on the task of realising the toothy titular creatures for *Gremlins 2*

Opposite: *Baker poses with a few of his Gremlins creations.*
Left: *Kevin Peter Hall in Baker's expressive mechanical make-up for* Harry and the Hendersons.

The New Batch, the anarchic sequel to Joe Dante's 1984 mini-monsterfest. A mammoth task, it required Baker to employ a crew of more than eighty artists and technicians, and the setting up of a gremlin production line to churn out the 300 plus puppets required of the script. It was not, however, a project Baker particularly relished or indeed wanted.

Right: *Edward G. Robinson as a mogwai!* **Below:** *Baker's workshop taken over by Gremlins!*

"I turned it down many times but Warner Brothers refused to accept that, and basically said, 'What can we do to make it more appealing to you?'" Baker's reply was: "'Let me re-design the gremlins, let's make *characters* out of them.' I thought Chris Walas' stuff in the first film was great, especially for the time and money he had. But all the gremlins were the same — except he put a furry stripe on one. They were all out of the same mould. I said, 'Let's make them *different*.'"

Baker got his wish, and a lot more besides. In addition to the 175 generic gremlins used for crowd scenes, Baker and his crew had to produce ten versions of Gizmo, four versions of each of the other four main gremlin characters (Lenny, George, Mohawk and Daffy), a flying bat gremlin, a vegetable gremlin, a girlie gremlin, a spider gremlin, plus a number of mutations for the lab scene: "There was a lot of stuff. I had a big crew, a lot of people to baby-sit. But it was actually a really enjoyable experience. I got to love coming to work, just to be with those guys who were my friends. And I'm pleased we managed to make as much stuff as we did and keep a certain quality to it. I don't think it's the best work we've ever done, but the puppets were pretty good — they weren't just simple paint jobs. And after we had made them, we'd sit there and play with them, and I'd ask myself, 'How lucky am I?'"

Unfortunately for Baker, his luck seemed to run out, as his next two major projects both ended up being as disappointing as the aborted *Night Skies*, a film about eleven malevolent aliens Baker was working on for Steven Speilberg before the project was dropped in favour of *E.T.*. Representing more than two years' work, Baker's involvement in them meant his having to turn down a number of high-profile movies, one of which was David Cronenberg's adaptation of William S. Burroughs' infamous novel *Naked Lunch* (1992). Having worked with Cronenberg on *Videodrome*, Baker was keen to renew their partnership. However, Cronenberg's script called for Baker to provide a host of sexually explicit effects, something which he found difficult to reconcile with his new role as a father: "I had been talking to David and then someone else came to me and said, 'I want to make this film called *Rex* about a little girl who finds this little bitty dinosaur egg, it hatches, grows up and becomes her pet — it's a really nice kind of family film.' So it was, 'Hmmm. A movie like *Naked Lunch* with its subject matter, or this dinosaur thing? I think I'll do the dinosaur!'"

For Baker, it would prove to be the wrong decision. After nearly a year of intensive labour, the film was cancelled, with Baker forced to hand over all his work to the film's producers, who subsequently completed the project in Japan without Baker's participation: "We were doing some real neat dinosaur stuff, some work I think was going to blow people away."

Baker's next project suffered a similar fate. *Isobar*, a futuristic updating of the Christopher Lee/Peter Cushing film *Horror Express* (1972), was set to star Sylvester Stallone. But again, after ten months of work, the project was put into turnaround, though Baker hopes it may still get made: "It's disappointing to spend ten months of your life and waste it like that. You do this work, and you have a lot of fun. But it's also really cool to go to the theatre and have people respond to it. We did some really neat stuff, we made this really neat monster that had these cool tentacles. But it was going to be a nightmare to shoot. I kept saying to my crew, 'This is going to be the one where I'm standing on the set and the director's screaming at me, "How many takes is it going to take to do this?"' Because this creature had tentacles everywhere. I just knew it was going to tie itself in a big knot."

These two cancelled movies left a big gap in Baker's filmography, although he did manage to fit in a contribution to *The Rocketeer* (1991), Joe Johnston's homage to thirties Hollywood. Baker made up the ironically named seven foot tall Tiny Ron to look like Rondo Hatton, a B-movie actor from the thirties and early forties who suffered from congenital acromegaly of the face and body, and as a result was cast solely as monsters or mad killers because, it was said, "he needed no make-up". "It was kind of a labour of love," states Baker, "I wanted to do it, there wasn't any money, but it was kind of fun because I like Rondo."

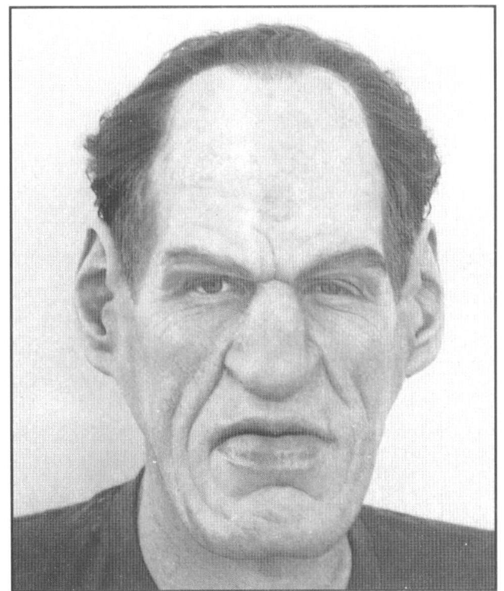

***Above:** A vegetable mutant!*
***Left:** A personal project for Baker — Tiny Ron in Rondo Hatton-esque make-up.*

"I do realise I have had an impact on the make-up effects business," states Rick Baker. "The main thing I think I've contributed is an enthusiasm for the stuff, and I'll probably be remembered more for people I started out and trained. When I was first doing make-up I was young and all the other make-up artists were like fifty years old. And what I think inspired a lot of younger kids to get into the stuff was the fact that here I was, a kid with long hair, wearing a t-shirt, managing to do some neat stuff, and them thinking, 'Hey! I can do that to.' I think it was that, more than anything else, that and the fact that I had a love for what I did and wanted to do work that was *really* good. It wasn't just a job to me, it was like an obsession. I think that's where I helped, I think my work inspired a lot of people who might have been fine artists and used their talents somewhere else to say, 'Yes, this is cool, I'd like to do something like that.' I used to be the kid that did the stuff – now I'm considered an old-timer."

Despite the pressures and occasional disappointments, Baker says he has lost neither his enthusiasm nor passion for his craft: "Although there was a time right after *Greystoke* when I got really burned out, I feel really fortunate that I had this obsession. Now I'm in my early forties I realise I've missed a lot in life, but I don't regret it." ■

Chapter Thirteen

He's back!

Stan Winston's work on Terminator 2: Judgment Day

With *Terminator 2: Judgment Day,* director James Cameron and creature creator Stan Winston continued their successful partnership, returning to the characters and situations that had helped make both their names. Initially Cameron predicted Winston's effects workload would be minimal, since he envisaged the majority would be created using the then burgeoning computer-graphics technology, and Winston would simply create a series of deterioration make-ups on Arnold Schwarzenegger, reprising his role as the Terminator. But the cost of realising all of Cameron's and co-screenwriter William Wisher's ideas with CGI proved too much. Consequently, Cameron replaced many of the intended CGI shots with mechanical and make-up effects, increasing Winston's workload dramat-

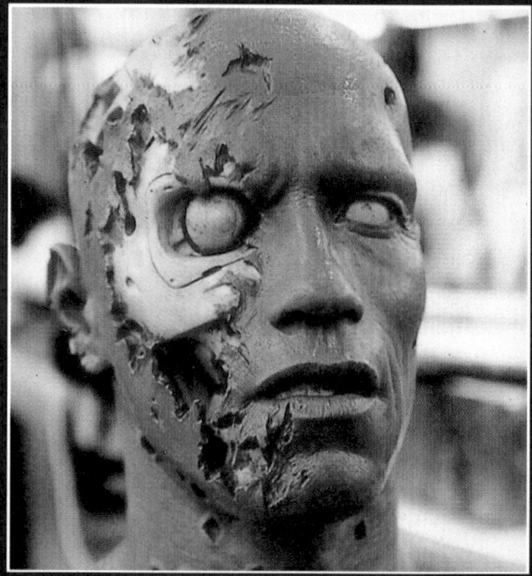

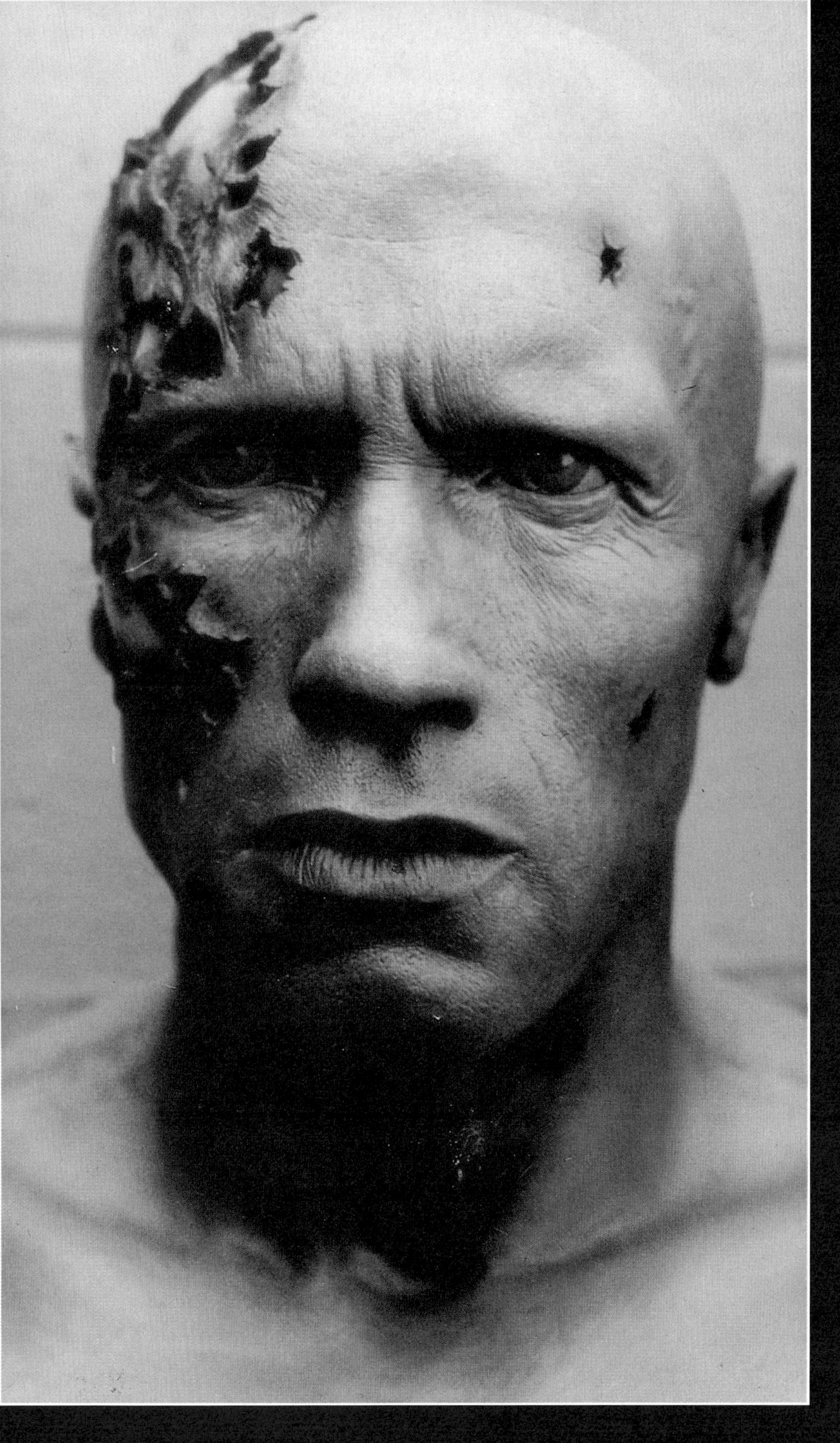

Opposite top: *The Terminator's damaged head in clay.*
Opposite bottom: *Schwarzenegger in full Terminator make-up.*
Left: *One of the many convincing Arnold Schwarzenegger puppet heads.*

Right: *The Cyberdyne puppet on set.*
Below: *The T-1000's head.*

TERMINATOR 2 CYBERDYNE PUPPET

For the scene in *Terminator 2* in which Arnold Schwarzenegger's Terminator takes on a SWAT team in the foyer of the Cyberdyne Building, James Cameron's script called for Schwarzenegger to receive a number of bullet hits in the face. Since this couldn't be pulled off using the actor, Stan Winston and his crew constructed a head-to-hips puppet Arnie specifically for this purpose.

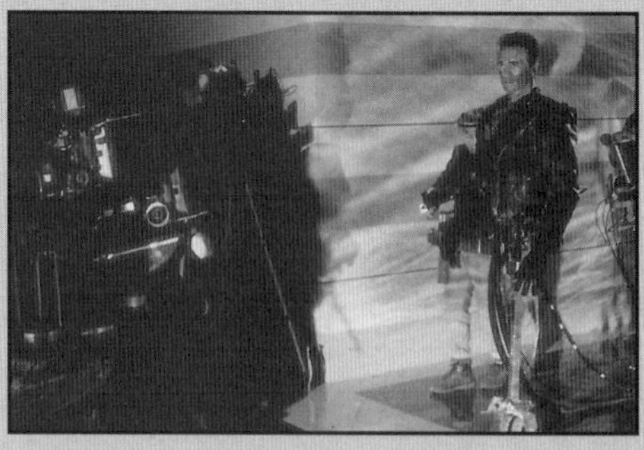

From a body cast of Schwarzenegger, Winston's crew made a fibreglass torso of the actor, topped with an endoskeleton skull covered by a foam latex skin made from a lifecast of Arnie. Underneath this skin several explosive charges called squibs were placed. When detonated, these squibs would simulate bullet hits.

To make the puppet move forward, it was attached to a wheel base and pushed along by a puppeteer (Shane Mahan), who was linked to it by a boom arm. As the puppeteer moved forward, so his movements were transferred to the puppet. He also controlled the puppet's arms, using a pair of thin black rods. Three additional puppeteers were needed to operate the puppet's hip, shoulders and facial movements, using a combination of radio and cable controls.

To ensure a near perfect match between the puppet Arnie and the real thing, Mahan studied footage of Schwarzenegger walking, while the actor in turn studied the puppet's gait and tried to match it. ■

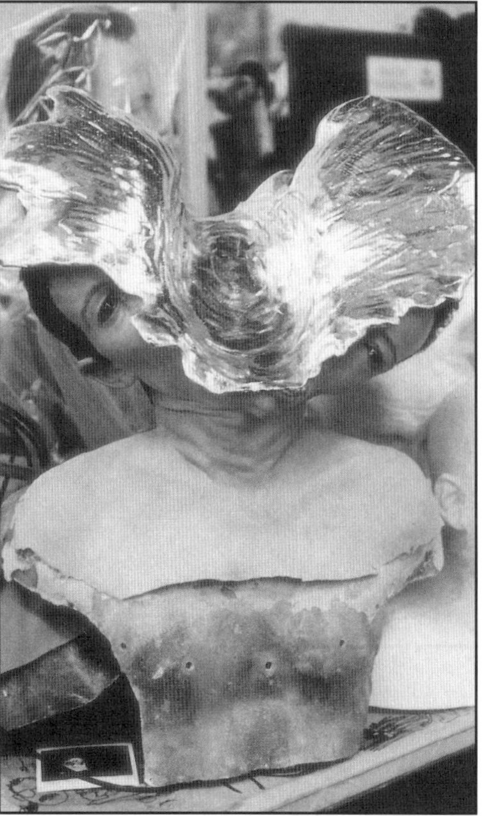

ically: "Jim came up with hundreds of insane, impossible effects. There were more in the first two minutes of this script than in the entire first movie."

Although a large portion of Winston's effort would be taken up depicting the various stages of damage sustained by the Terminator battling his nemesis, the protean liquid-metal T-1000 Terminator (played in its human form by Robert Patrick), these effects were, to a certain extent, a known quantity. Though Winston still had to create a pair of articulated Terminator puppets — one to show bullet hits on Schwarzenegger's face during the SWAT team's attack on the Cyberdyne building; the second used at the film's climax when he is impaled to the steel mill floor by a metal pole — it was those concerning the T-1000 that proved to be most challenging to Winston and his crew, with them having to provide numerous body appliances and full-size puppets, each detailing the T-1000's varying injuries. To create the bloodless bullet hits in Patrick's chest, Winston devised a number of chrome craters that sprang open on cue. Later in post-production, Industrial Light & Magic, George Lucas' effects company who handled all the film's show-stop-

Far left: *Winston studies a cast of Schwarzenegger's head.*
Left: *A dummy Robert Patrick, having been sliced with a metal pole.*
Below: *One of the two Splash Head puppets.*

ping morphing effects, used Winston's designs to reverse the process and show the wounds healing.

Though simple in concept, some of the most difficult effects to perfect were the various chrome 'blade' arms used by the T-1000 as either weapons or tools throughout the movie. According to Winston, while not difficult to design or construct, the 'blade' arms, once chromed, revealed every imperfection in their original sculpture and therefore required many attempts to achieve the desired polished-metal effect.

The most dramatic examples of Winston's work, however, can be seen during the three sequences in which the severest damage is inflicted upon the T-1000. For each of these sequences, a number of puppets were created, nicknamed Splash Head, Donut Head and Pretzel Man. The first can be seen when Schwarzenegger's Terminator helps Sarah Connor (played by Linda Hamilton) break out of the hospital. As the T-1000 pries open the lift doors with its crowbar arms, the Terminator fires point blank at its head with a shotgun, splitting it apart, an effect that utilised two puppet heads and an appliance on Robert Patrick's double.

Both the Donut Head and Pretzel Man effects appear in the steel mill sequence at the film's climax. The former when Hamilton fires off a close-range shot at the T-1000, resulting in a large hole in its head. The latter when the crippled Terminator shoots a grenade at the T-1000's stomach causing him to burst open, before tumbling back into a pit of molten metal. The Donut Head was a relatively simple head and shoulders puppet with radio-controlled eye and jaw mechanisms, while the Pretzel Man was in fact three puppets. The first was triggered to spring into the pre-sculpted 'pretzel' shape, while the second, which teeters on the gantry ledge over-looking the molten metal pit, was a more-detailed, articulated affair, puppeteered from below by rods and cables. The third was simply a weighted dummy rigged to fall into the molten steel.

In addition, Winston and his crew created four endoskeletons for use in the film's future war prologue, three puppets of Linda Hamilton that are blasted by the nuclear shockwave in Sarah Connor's nightmare, a fake Schwarzenegger head for a deleted scene in which Hamilton reprogrammes the Terminator to make him more human, plus a complex series of prosthetic limbs and a fragile resin dummy for the sequence in which the T-1000 freezes and is subsequently blown into tiny shards. In all, Winston calculated that his crew realised some 300 separate make-up and animatronic gags. "With *Terminator 2* we were able to bring all the knowledge and experience gained in the five years since *The Terminator* into the project. As film-makers we hope to make the sequel better than the original — to do everything we did before, but bigger, better. We have to forget the statement 'less is more.' In effects, at least, *more* is more." ■

Chapter Fourteen

Sixty-five million years in the making

Stan Winston and Jurassic Park

When Steven Spielberg first began adapting *Jurassic Park*, Michael Crichton's best-selling novel revolving around genetically-engineered dinosaurs running amok in a theme park, his main concern was whether he could convincingly portray the enormous amount of dinosaurs the story called for. These included a 5,000 lb tyrannosaurus rex, a pride of vicious velociraptors, a sickly triceratops, a venom-spitting dilophosaurus and a tree-munching brachiosaur. Rather than rely on traditional methods of creating cinematic dinosaurs, such as stop-motion or go-motion, Spielberg was determined to film as many of his dinosaurs as possible 'live' on set, using full-size animatronic creatures which could interact with his actors. "Right from the start I thought we would be able to create mechanical dinosaurs that were a far cry from the shark in *Jaws*."

And so in December 1990, a full two-and-a-half years before *Jurassic Park* (1993) reached the theatres, Spielberg and his producer, Kathleen Kennedy, approached Stan Winston, who Spielberg had almost worked with on *E.T.*, to discuss the feasibility of creating *Jurassic Park*'s dinosaur cast.

"I thought Stan had the best monster shop in Hollywood," recalls Spielberg, "and that he would really be able to solve the purely mechanical, logistical problems that occur when you try to create a natural-looking, fast-moving, twenty-

Opposite: *Stan Winston's impressive hydraulic tyrannosaurus rex.*
Left: *The tyrannosaurus rex on the loose!*

***Top:** Winston working on a velociraptor sculpt.* ***Above:** The hydraulic tyrannosaurus rex up close.*

three foot tyrannosaurus rex, or an eighteen foot long brachiosaur's neck and head. I thought Stan had the mechanical savvy to figure out the problems and be successful."

Though still working on *Terminator 2*, Winston immediately assigned his studio's top artists the task of conceptualising *Jurassic Park*'s dinosaurs before a contract was signed or the film had even been given the final go-ahead by Universal Pictures. So while Spielberg went off to direct *Hook* (1991), Winston set about translating his artists' sketches into living, breathing three-dimensions, initially producing fifth-scale models which were then scaled up to life-size and re-sculpted in clay, before being moulded and cast in foam latex. "No one had done big dinosaurs before, but someone *had* done a big alien," remarks Winston. "I was the person who had come closest to doing something like it."

For the film's crowning achievement, the twenty foot plus tall tyrannosaurus rex, Winston's crew built a massive internal hydraulic system to provide the creature's full range of movements. Split into two sections, the tyrannosaurus' head, torso and tail were mounted on a customised flight simulator — dubbed the 'dino simulator' — which was rigged to a computer control system, in turn linked to a miniature tyrannosaurus operated by a team of puppeteers. The puppeteers' movements could then be recorded, while for shots of the rex's legs meeting the ground, a moving platform was constructed that featured the creature's underbelly, as well as hydraulic legs and a tail. Winston's crew also constructed a separate tyrannosaurus head with extra detailing and more mechanics, which was used for close-up work and featured a complete range of facial movements.

For the velociraptors, the film's ferocious killing machines whose movements, in direct contrast to those of the lumbering tyrannosaurus, were to be swift and agile, Winston employed both high and low-tech approaches. These ranged from a man-in-a-raptor-suit to a series of mechanical, cable-operated puppets whose movements were supplemented with radio-controlled mechanisms and concealed rods.

But while Spielberg hoped to get much of the dinosaur footage live, he understood that certain shots — full-body views of the tyrannosaurus walking and running — would have to be obtained by other means. While the water pseudo-pod featured in *The Abyss* and the shape-shifting liquid-metal T-1000 terminator in *Terminator 2* had thrilled audiences and shown the potential of computer-generated imagery (CGI) in feature films, up until then CGI had only really been successful in portraying metallic or non-organic entities. *Jurassic Park* was to be the movie to show that CGI could, in fact, convincingly duplicate living, breathing creatures — an area that had hitherto been the domain of rubber. The question that was inevitably asked following its release was: Is this the end of make-up effects?

For Winston, together with ILM who won an Oscar for the film's visual effects, the question is almost an irrelevant one. He stresses that of the fourteen minutes of dinosaur footage seen in *Jurassic Park*, more than two-thirds are live action and are *his* creations, and while the CGI is indeed exceptional, it's the skill of the director and editor that makes each facet complement each other perfectly. "The seamless blend between the live action and the computer animation is incredible. Each technique sells the other so well you're not aware of any technique at all. The audience may *think* they know what they're seeing, but they don't."

Indeed, Winston sees the advent of computers extremely positively, as an extra item in his toolbox, rather than the proverbial nail in his craft's coffin.

"People say, 'God, is that going to replace what you do?' But how can anything replace art? Computers are *not* here to jeopardise people who do live-action creature or character effects. Computers just allow us to do more. I have a CGI unit in my studio, but it will *never* replace what you need as an artist to create the character — it'll never completely replace live-action. In the future you may have a movie that is completely computer-generated, as we have completely animated films today. But they are not going to *replace* live-action. It's a new art form, a new piece of entertainment — it's good, it's fun, it's neat. It's here, it's the future, *I've done dinosaurs — I don't want to become one.*"

Rick Baker, however, remains a touch more pragmatic about the computer revolution.

"The computer is definitely going to take a chunk out of our business — it already has. A lot of the guys who've worked for me are sweating. It is going to change the business — but it's still just a great tool. You can do things with a computer that you can't do with rubber, there's no doubt about it. With *The Thing*, people thought we could do anything; even with *American Werewolf* people were thinking these guys can do anything — and we *knew* we couldn't. What we usually did was some fancy foot work to get around the things we couldn't do, and come up with a suggestion of something else.

"The computer *can* do things that we can't. But as long as there are special effects people like Rob Bottin who've got crazy imaginations, I'm sure we can still come out with some neat stuff. Having said that, there's so much saturation of this kind of rubber stuff — it just doesn't have the impact it once did. And I can definitely see the end of make-up effects. Though I still think we *can* do things with rubber that they can't. Fortunately a lot of what I do is hairy stuff, and they're still having trouble making something that looks like hair. *Thank God.*"

***Below:** A test puppet of the tyrannosaurus rex.*

"Some people are very pessimistic about it, and think it's the end of everything," muses the godfather of make-up effects, Dick Smith. "I really don't think so. I believe there *will* be a loss of certain things, but I still have faith that there will always be appliance make-ups and similarly creative things to be done, even if we're only making the models from which the computer images are then generated."

"On *Jurassic Park*, all the dinosaurs were designed here," Winston concludes. "*Every* dinosaur. Whether they were live-action or not, there is one common artistic eye. What I have learned with *Jurassic Park*, because I have a pride of ownership, is that I don't want to develop characters, the art, and give it to somebody else to do, when *I* could do it, had I the proper tools here. It was *T2* and *Jurassic Park* that made me realise I needed to add a new tool, which was CGI. I mean, I take computers as a positive new tool. The most negative thing about them is that there are more things to think about and learn. And that's not negative. That just means, 'You ain't done yet, you're *still* going to school guys.'" ■

Opposite: *Winston's animatronic raptors on the jungle set.* ***Right:*** *The tyrannosaurus stalks its prey.* ***Below:*** *Director Steven Spielberg and co-producer Kathleen Kennedy pose with Winston's sickly triceratops.*

Appendix 1

Filmographies

RICK BAKER

Year	Film	Director
1971	Octaman	Harry Essex
1972	The Thing with Two Heads	Lee Frost
1972	Bone	Larry Cohen
1973	Black Caesar	Larry Cohen
1973	Live and Let Die	Guy Hamilton
1973	Schlock	John Landis
1973	The Exorcist	William Friedkin
1974	Flesh Gordon	Michael Beveniste/ Howard Ziehm
1974	It's Alive	Larry Cohen
1974	The Autobiography of Miss Jane Pittman (TV)	John Korty
1975	Death Race 2000	Paul Bartel
1976	Squirm	Jeff Lieberman
1976	King Kong	John Guillermin
1977	Zebra Force	Joe Tornatore
1977	The Kentucky Fried Movie	John Landis
1977	Star Wars	George Lucas
1978	The Incredible Melting Man	William Sachs
1978	The Fury	Brian De Palma
1978	The Funhouse: Carnival of Terror	Tobe Hooper
1978	It Lives Again	Larry Cohen
1980	The Warning	Greydon Clark
1980	Tanya's Island	Alfred Sole
1981	The Howling	Joe Dante
1981	The Incredible Shrinking Woman	Joel Schumacher
1981	Ghost Story	John Irvin
1981	An American Werewolf in London (ACADEMY AWARD)	John Landis
1982	Videodrome	David Cronenberg
1984	Greystoke: The Legend of Tarzan, Lord of the Apes	Hugh Hudson
1984	Starman	John Carpenter
1985	Cocoon (consultant)	Ron Howard
1985	My Science Project	Jonathan Betuel
1986	Max Mon Amour (chimpanzee consultant)	Nagisa Oshima
1986	Ratboy	Sondra Locke
1987	It's Alive III: Island of the Alive	Larry Cohen
1987	Summer School	Carl Reiner
1987	Harry and the Hendersons (ACADEMY AWARD)	William Dear

1988	Coming to America	John Landis
1988	Gorillas in the Mist	Michael Apted
1988	Moonwalker	Colin Chivers
1989	Missing Link	David Hughes/ Carol Hughes
1990	Gremlins 2 The New Batch	Joe Dante
1991	The Rocketeer	Joe Johnston
1992	Lorenzo's Oil (prosthetics consultant)	George Miller
1994	Wolf	Mike Nichols
1994	Baby's Day Out	Patrick Read Johnson

ROB BOTTIN

Year	Film	Director
1976	Squirm	Jeff Lieberman
1976	King Kong	John Guillermin
1977	Star Wars	George Lucas
1978	The Incredible Melting Man	William Sachs
1978	The Fury	Brian De Palma
1978	Piranha	Joe Dante
1979	Rock 'n' Roll High School	Allan Arkush
1980	Humanoids from the Deep	Barbara Peeters
1980	Tanya's Island	Alfred Sole
1980	The Fog	John Carpenter
1980	Airplane!	Jim Abrahams/ Jerry Zucker/ David Zucker
1981	The Howling	Joe Dante
1982	The Thing	John Carpenter
1983	Twilight Zone: The Movie	Joe Dante
1985	Legend	Ridley Scott
1985	Explorers	Joe Dante
1987	InnerSpace	Joe Dante
1987	The Witches of Eastwick	George Miller
1987	RoboCop	Paul Verhoeven
1988	The Great Outdoors	Howard Deutch
1990	RoboCop 2	Irvin Kershner
1990	Total Recall (ACADEMY AWARD)	Paul Verhoeven
1991	RoboCop 3	Fred Dekker
1991	Bugsy	Barry Levinson
1992	Basic Instinct	Paul Verhoeven
1993	Toys	Barry Levinson

STEVE JOHNSON

Year	Film	Director
1977	Galactic Connection	
1980	Tanya's Island	Alfred Sole
1980	The Fog	John Carpenter
1980	Airplane!	Jim Abrahams/ Jerry Zucker/ David Zucker
1980	Humanoids from the Deep	Barbara Peeters
1981	The Howling	Joe Dante

1981	An American Werewolf in London	John Landis
1981	Ghost Story	John Irvin
1982	Videodrome	David Cronenberg
1984	Greystoke: The Legend of Tarzan, Lord of the Apes	Hugh Hudson
1984	Ghostbusters	Ivan Reitman
1985	Fright Night	Tom Holland
1985	Howling II: Your Sister is a Werewolf	Philippe Mora
1986	Poltergeist 2: The Other Side	Brian Gibson
1986	Solarbabies	Alan Johnson
1986	Big Trouble in Little China	John Carpenter
1987	Predator	John McTiernan
1987	Night of the Demons	Kevin S. Tenney
1988	Howling IV: The Original Nightmare	John Hough
1988	Dead Heat	Mark Goldblatt
1988	A Nightmare on Elm Street IV: The Dream Master	Renny Harlin
1989	The Abyss	James Cameron
1990	Highway to Hell	Ate de Jong
1990	The Guardian	William Friedkin
1990	Howling VI: The Freaks	Hope Perello
1991	Suburban Commando	Burt Kennedy
1991	The Rapture	Michael Tolkin
1992	Brain Donors	Dennis Dugan
1992	Batman Returns	Tim Burton
1992	Pet Sematary II	Mary Lambert
1992	Innocent Blood	John Landis
1993	Freaked	Alex Winter/Tom Stern
1993	The Temp	Tom Holland
1993	Even Cowgirls Get the Blues	Gus Van Sant
1993	Return of the Living Dead Part III	Brian Yuzna
1993	The Stand (TV)	Mick Garris
1994	Brainscan	John Fiynn

DICK SMITH

Date	Film	Director
1959	Misty	James B. Clark
1962	Requiem for a Heavyweight	Ralph Nelson
1963	It's a Mad Mad Mad Mad World	Stanley Kramer
1963	All the Way Home	Alex Segal
1963	The Cardinal	Otto Preminger
1964	The World of Henry Orient	George Roy Hill
1965	Marco the Magnificent	Denys De La Patelliere
1965	Harvey Middleman, Fireman	Ernest Pintoff
1967	Mark Twain Tonight! (TV)	Peter Bogart
1969	Midnight Cowboy	John Schlesinger
1969	Me, Natalie	Fred Coe
1970	Little Big Man	Arthur Penn
1970	House of Dark Shadows	Dan Curtis
1971	Who is Harry Kellerman and Why is He Saying Those Terrible Things About Me?	Ulu Grosbard
1972	The Godfather	Francis Ford Coppola
1973	The Exorcist	William Friedkin
1974	The Godfather Part II	Francis Ford Coppola
1974	The Stepford Wives	Bryan Forbes
1975	The Sunshine Boys	Herbert Ross

1976	Taxi Driver	Martin Scorsese
1976	Marathon Man	John Schlesinger
1976	Burnt Offerings	Dan Curtis
1977	The Sentinel	Michael Winner
1977	Exorcist 2: The Heretic	John Boorman
1978	The Fury	Brian De Palma
1978	The Deer Hunter	Michael Cimino
1980	Altered States	Ken Russell
1980	The Dogs of War	John Irvin
1981	Nighthawks	Bruce Malmuth
1981	Scanners	David Cronenberg
1981	The Fan	Edward Bianchi
1981	Ghost Story	John Irvin
1983	The Hunger	Tony Scott
1984	Amadeus (ACADEMY AWARD)	Milos Forman
1984	Starman	John Carpenter
1988	Poltergeist III: The Other Side	Gary Sherman
1988	Everybody's All-American	Taylor Hackford
1988	Sweet Home (Japanese)	
1989	Dad	Gary David Goldberg
1992	Death Becomes Her	Robert Zemeckis
1992	Forever Young	Steve Miner

STAN WINSTON

Year	Film	Director
1972	Gargoyles (TV)	B.W.L. Norton
1972	Blacula	William Crain
1974	The Autobiography of Miss Jane Pittman (TV)	John Korty
1976	W.C. Fields and Me	Arthur Hiller
1977	Mansion of the Doomed	Michael Pataki
1977	Dracula's Dog	Albert Band
1978	The Wiz	Sidney Lumet
1980	The Exterminator	James Glickenhaus
1981	Dead and Buried	Gary A. Sherman
1981	Heartbeeps	Allan Arkush
1982	Parasite	Charles Band
1983	The Entity	Sidney J. Furie
1983	Something Wicked This Way Comes	Jack Clayton
1984	The Terminator	James Cameron
1985	Chiller (TV)	Wes Craven
1986	Invaders from Mars	Tobe Hooper
1986	Aliens (ACADEMY AWARD)	James Cameron
1987	The Monster Squad	Fred Dekker
1987	Predator	John McTiernan
1988	Pumpkinhead	Stan Winston
1988	Alien Nation	Graham Baker
1989	Leviathan	George Pan Cosmatos
1990	Predator 2	Stephen Hopkins
1990	Edward Scissorhands	Tim Burton
1991	Terminator 2: Judgment Day (ACADEMY AWARD)	James Cameron
1991	A Gnome Named Gnorm	Stan Winston
1992	Batman Returns	Tim Burton
1993	Jurassic Park (ACADEMY AWARD)	Steven Spielberg
1994	Interview with the Vampire	Neil Jordan

Bibliography

BIBLIOGRAPHY

We are indebted to

Books

Film Tricks Special Effects in the Movies (Harlin Quist) Harold Schecteer and David Everitt
Nightmare Movies (Bloomsbury) Kim Newman
Science Fiction Image (Columbus Books) Gene Wright
Making a Monster (Crown) Al Taylor and Sue Roy
Leonard Maltin's Movie and Video Guide 1993 Edition (Signet) Edited by Leonard Maltin
The Primal Scream (Orbit) John Brosnan
The Time Out Film Guide (Penguin) Edited by Tom Milne
The Making of Jurassic Park (Ballantine) Don Shay and Jody Duncan
The Making of Terminator 2: Judgment Day (Titan) Don Shay and Jody Duncan

Magazines

Cinefantastique   *Cinefex*   *Entertainment Weekly*   *Fangoria*   *Starlog*   *Video Watchdog*

TV

Moving Pictures, BBC2

USEFUL ADDRESSES

UK

Strand Glass, 109 High Street, Brentford, Middlesex TW8 8AZ for fibreglass, latex, moulding rubbers, resins, polyurethane foam.

Alec Tiranti Ltd, 27 Warren Street, London W1 & 70 High Street, Theale, Reading RG7 5AR for modelling clay, sculpting tools, armature wire, plaster.

Screen Face, Mitastyle Limited, 24 Powis Terrace, Notting Hill Gate, London for foam-latex, film blood, latex, gelatines, alginate, rubber-mask grease-paint, prosthetic adhesives and removers, make-up supplies.

Charles H. Fox Ltd, 22 Tavistock Street, London WC2E for rubber mask grease paints, liquid latex, foam latex kits, rubber noses and chins, make-up books, hair, cosmetics, plaster bandage, prosthetic adhesives and general make-up supplies.

USA

Burman Industries Incorporated, 14141 Covello Street, Suite 6-A, Van Nuys, CA 91405 for alginates, adhesives, foam latex, dental acrylic, stones and plaster.

Kryolan Corporation, 132 Ninth Street, San Francisco, CA 94103 for make-up, latex and foam systems, hair and wig making items, bloods and gelatins, adhesives and removers.

Appendix 3

Index

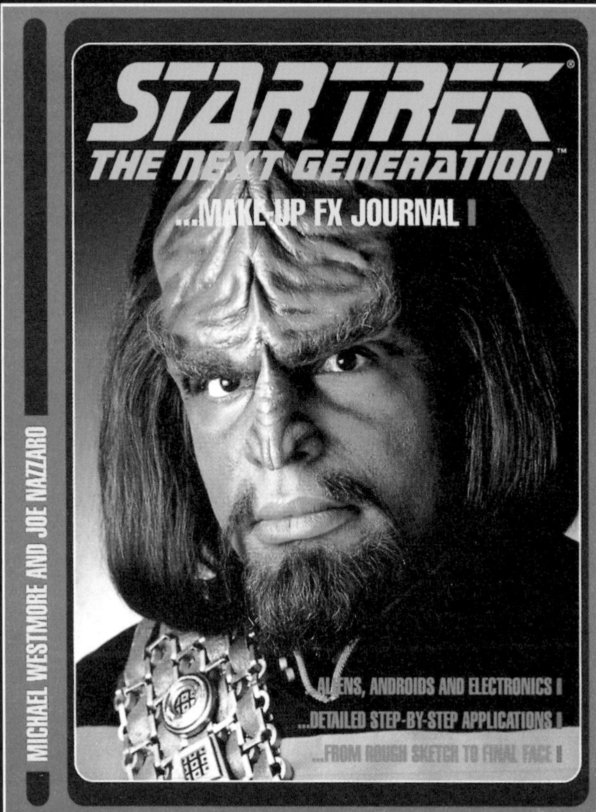

For a catalogue of all Titan's film and TV publications, please send a large stamped SAE to Titan Books Mail Order, 42-44 Dolben Street, London SE1 0UP. Please quote reference BTM on both envelopes.